BARTHOLDI

AND THE

STATUE

OF

LIBERTY

Frédéric Auguste Bartholdi (Aug. 2, 1834–Oct. 4, 1904), with two of his best-known statues, the Statue of Liberty and the Lion of Belfort

BARTHOLDI

AND THE

STATUE

OF

LIBERTY

WILLADENE PRICE

WITH 42 ILLUSTRATIONS

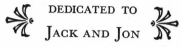

DEDICATED TO
JACK AND JON

BARTHOLDI
AND THE
STATUE
OF
LIBERTY

CONTENTS

LIST OF ILLUSTRATIONS

1

"YOUR PATH IS IN SCULPTURING"

THE little French boy was deliciously happy as he sat by the banks of the River Lauch eating great handfuls of juicy blue grapes. "What a wonderful life it would be," thought Frédéric Auguste Bartholdi, "if we could stay in Colmar always and never have to go back to Paris to school."

Here, right in his own shady garden, he could sit for hours and look way down the river and see the long, low fishing boats looking like sailing vineyards carrying their sweet cargo to the city market. He sometimes dreamed of being a sailor. If he wanted to, he could lie on his back and see the fat, rounded tops of the Vosges hills. Or, if he were in an imaginative mood, he would think of the three towers of a crumbling old castle near the edge of his garden and imagine himself a brave young knight. Just lying there and looking at the spire of the great Cathedral made him feel warm and secure.

Many times Auguste and his brother Charles would bring paper and pencil to the little house in the garden. Charles, who was older and being tutored in art, would make sketches while Auguste watched. All went well as long as Auguste admired Charles's drawings. But if Auguste suggested changing a line here and there, Charles

11

Sculptured sun, moved from the front door, now appears on the fireplace in the Bartholdi library

jumped up in a fury and chased him away. Usually the scuffle continued until Charles finally pushed Auguste out the door, showering pencils and paper after him. A loud bang of the door and a click of the latch ended the argument so far as Charles was concerned.

Auguste, in high good humor, and never one to give up easily, would gather up the pencils and paper he had been bombarded with, place himself comfortably on the cool green carpet of grass outside the door, and await his brother. He amused himself by making dozens of drawings of the sculptured sun which was mounted over the carved front door. The sun had a grim face with wriggly rays all around it. Auguste claimed that when he looked at this funny sun a long time, it blinked its eyes at him. In any event he felt that the sun was a real member of his family.

The garden house had originally belonged to Great Grandmother's family whose name was Sonntag—a German name which means "day of sun." Auguste was glad Great Grandfather Gilles-Francois Bartholdi, who was a popular pharmacist in Colmar, had been very careful not to disturb the sun when he bought the house from the Sonntag family and remodeled it.

Some days Mama sat on the stone bench under one of the old ivy-covered trees and told stories about the gay parties she and Papa used to have in the garden house. The boys thought it fun just to look at Mama. She was so pretty in her full skirt all embroidered in flowers and her white lace blouse with big sleeves. Her dark eyes sparkled when she told about the happy days when Papa was still alive and his friends—the mayor, the lawyer, artists, and writers—came often to spend long summer evenings discussing literature and art as well as affairs of government.

Most times there were relatives at the parties, too. There was Grandfather Bartholdi who was a doctor, and Uncle Charles Beysser, the judge, who was Mama's brother. Uncle Charles, who was very patriotic, liked to tell about the Great General Jean-Michel Beysser, who fought in the French Revolution and who was executed.

Charles could remember kind, generous Papa, who, even though he held the important position of Counsellor of the Prefecture of Colmar, was never too busy to listen to small boys. Auguste was only two when Papa died but he, too, could remember how much fun it was to ride piggyback on Papa's shoulders. Once when it began to sprinkle, they raced all the way from the river's edge of the garden,

"Wonderful wide wooden stairway" in Auguste's home. (Notice his baby carriage in the corner)

past the vineyards, into the big stone house. Even then they did not stop, but raced on up the wonderful wide wooden stairway, down the hall, and into the playroom.

If it happened not to be raining and if it were Thursday, the Bartholdis would all go down to the Market where farmers, fishermen, and seedsmen displayed their wares for sale.

Thursday was not only a day for marketing, but a day

for fun, too. Sometimes there would be a parade of drummer boys led by an old man and followed by would-be soldiers with toy rifles and sabres. Everywhere children were playing with kites and hoops. Often Auguste would join his good friend Chrétien Mugel under the big round tent for a game of ninepins. It was even fun to join the crowd around one of the city pumps to get a cool drink of water. At four o'clock everyone would go over to the National Stage Coach office in the Hotel of the Two Keys and watch the mail coach take off for Paris.

On the way home the Bartholdis would stop at the bake shop that smelled of warm, freshly cooked pretzels. (Years later, when Auguste got homesick for a bit of Colmar he would go out and buy himself a bag of pretzels. But never did he find any quite as good as those baked in the little shop beside the old city gate.)

Then they would head down the winding alleys past all the houses with the pointed roofs to Number 30, Merchant's Street. Here they pushed open a heavy gate and walked through a covered passageway to their own courtyard.

By ten o'clock all the city was quiet. Even the older boys and girls who had strolled outside the city wall made certain to be home before the gates were locked and the deep tone of the clock in the old bell tower boomed out the curfew.

All that was long ago. Now, in the year 1843, Auguste was nine, and each year the widow Charlotte Beysser Bartholdi took her two sons to Paris for the school season. Auguste was not a very good student. In fact, one of his first teachers wrote: "Conduct rather fickle. Work inconsistent. Lessons often badly prepared." Auguste thought it

Courtyard of the Bartholdi home in Colmar which is now a museum

more fun to take his table knife to his study room and carve a piece of wood than it was to pore over difficult textbooks. Madame Bartholdi, too, studied ancient languages and other subjects so that she could sometimes help her boys with their lessons.

As Auguste grew older, the summers in Colmar became more than just a happy vacation from schooldays. He and his brother were always included in the gatherings of family friends. Madame Bartholdi brought to her friends firsthand news of the growing unrest in Paris under the reign of Louis Philippe. But it was to the conversations about art and literature that Auguste listened most attentively.

Among the frequent guests was Théophile Schuler, a

popular artist and illustrator of books. Auguste was often inspired to go to the garden house and work for hours fashioning a bit of clay into one of Schuler's lively book characters. Finally Madame Bartholdi, upon the insistent advice of her friends, allowed Auguste to take art lessons from Martin Rossbach, a professor of design in the Community College of Colmar. These were happy times, indeed, for Auguste.

The townspeople of Colmar soon recognized his ability. Summers later, when they founded a museum in an ancient convent, Auguste was asked to fashion a statue in memory of Agnes, the founder of the convent. His Agnes, wearing a crown and holding a small figure of the convent chapel, was one of his first serious attempts at sculpturing.

As time went on, it became harder and harder for Auguste to concentrate on his studies. While now his teachers reported "work good enough," he spent as little time as possible at the Louis-le-Grand School and more and more in the student workshops of the sculptor Antoine Etex. Etex was the designer of some of the figures which decorate the famed Arch of Triumph and at the moment served as an ideal after which the imaginative Auguste aspired to pattern himself.

When Etex closed his doors to students, Auguste followed his brother Charles, who was studying painting in the workshops of the kindly artist Ary Scheffer. Here Auguste heard much talk of American liberty. Ary Scheffer had sympathy for the struggling young country across the sea. When he was a young man he had gone to live at the home of the sixty-year-old Marquis de Lafayette, where Benjamin Franklin and George Washington were considered as dear as the closest relative. Later Scheffer was commissioned by the French government to paint a portrait of the dashing young Lafayette who had contributed so much toward the American struggle for independence. The portrait was presented as a gift to the United States and now hangs in the House of Representatives.

Auguste also listened with wide-eyed curiosity to talk of the royal family. Scheffer was a frequent visitor at the Palace of the Tuilleries, not only as a personal friend of Louis Philippe, but as an instructor of art to the royal children.

In Ary Scheffer's studio Auguste found real fuel to kindle the smouldering fires of his vivid imagination. He loved the smell of paint and canvas. More often than not he forgot completely to do his lessons. Some days he would skip school entirely just to sit quietly in the corner of the studio and watch.

While Auguste was rebelling against his studies, the people of France were engaged in a more violent form of rebellion. They were blaming Louis Philippe for anything and everything that went wrong in France. Even if the weather was bad and there was a shortage of crops, they blamed the King.

So, much to Auguste's dismay, Ary Scheffer, who was a Captain in the National Guard, locked his studio and joined his regiment to do what he could to help the King. On the morning of February 24, 1848, Louis Philippe was rudely interrupted at breakfast and forced to sign his abdication. On this fateful morning Ary Scheffer and a fellow guardsman, the son of Lafayette, waited on the terrace beneath the windows of the King's private apartment

until the Queen beckoned to them. Then the two ran up
the steps, gathered the royal family together, and whisked
them off to a waiting carriage and eventual refuge in
England.

When the Bartholdis went to visit Colmar that summer, they left behind them a Paris smouldering with unrest. But, once they reached Alsace, their vacation was
marred but slightly by the rumblings of disorders in Paris.
In Colmar, as in other rural districts, the voters went
peacefully to the polls and cast their votes for president.
When the Bartholdis returned to Paris in the fall, Louis
Napoleon, who had won the office of president by the support of five and a half million French voters, was already
having his troubles with the National Assembly.

For Auguste, Paris was the same as always except that
Ary Scheffer was away in Holland. No doubt the Latin
professor at the Louis-le-Grand School noted an improvement at this time in Auguste's grades. Or perhaps it was
only an improvement in attendance.

In the middle of his last year in high school, Auguste's
teachers reported: "Great waste of time. No work. Class
attendance very irregular." Auguste was really a very
smart boy, but he lived only for art and studied only lessons that he felt would help him understand the mysteries
of great art.

Finally, his mother, who had long hoped Auguste
would aspire to be a lawyer and return to the pleasant
life of Colmar, stopped pleading with him. Thus Auguste
became an almost daily visitor to Ary Scheffer, who was
back in Paris and had again opened his doors to students.
Despite his eagerness, Auguste was uncertain of his own
ability. Once he took some wax home and worked for

hours fashioning a dog's head. Several times he carried his dog's head to the studio before he finally gained enough courage to show it to the master. When he did, Scheffer was amazed by its beauty and exclaimed: "My boy, your path is in sculpturing."

Once Madame Bartholdi had given her somewhat reluctant approval to an art career for her youngest son, she set about gaining his admittance to a Beaux-Arts school. But even though Auguste loved his mother dearly —so dearly in fact that he had given up early plans to be a sailor because he could not bear the thought of leaving her—he flatly refused to have any more formal schooling.

He was now seventeen years old. Everything he saw and heard concerning creative art left an impression on his eager mind. Under Louis Napoleon, there was continued unrest among the French people. In Paris there was frequently violence and rioting. One bleak, cold December evening in 1851 Auguste was walking home from the workshop when he saw something that may well have had a real influence on him later when he drew the design for our Statue of Liberty.

Some rioters who had intended to storm a barricade at the entrance of a gloomy street lost their courage and halted. Suddenly, out of the darkness, appeared a young girl. Holding a torch high, she sprang over the barricade shouting "Forward!". Just at that moment a shot rang out and, as she fell, her torch fired the barricade.

Auguste ran all the way home and sobbed out the wild story to his mother. He, who had grown up in a household where family tradition and love of France were a part of daily living, was beginning to realize the meaning of liberty.

2

A TRIP TO THE LAND OF COLOSSAL ART

EVEN though Auguste did not like to go to school, he did enjoy reading. He spent many hours searching among the bookstalls along the River Seine for a rare edition of some classic that had particularly interested him.

One late afternoon, when Auguste had grown weary of browsing in the bookstalls, he sat down at a table at one of the many little outdoor cafés to enjoy a huge plate of fried fish. He chose a place where he could look down the river, over the hodgepodge of fishermen, boats, and barges, and enjoy the outline of the Notre Dame Cathedral against the changing colors of the sunset.

He looked at that great pile of irregular shapes. "Why can't I," mused Auguste, "make a statue so big that it will stand out against the sunset for all to see."

The very next day he went to tell old Ary Scheffer about his desire to make a huge statue. The tired and graying painter did not laugh at Auguste. Instead, as Auguste was sure he would, he gave him some very sound advice. After all, Auguste did not forget that it was Ary Scheffer who had first recognized his ability as a sculptor. At a time when Auguste was quite content to dabble in paint, Scheffer insisted that he try his hand at modeling and had introduced him to the studio of the sculptor Jean-

François Soitoux. "If you want to do things on such a grand scale," said Scheffer, "you must first be an architect. How would you like to study with the man who restored the great Notre Dame Cathedral?"

So it was that Auguste began with slide rule and drawing board under the guidance of Eugène Viollet-le-duc. Later he studied with Henri Labrouste, an architect who was doing all manner of experiments with steel.

Each year, in Paris, the French government held an official art competition known as the Salon. Here artists from all over France brought their works to be displayed and judged. Auguste was anxious to participate in this competition. Even though he was still a student he was eager to create a work that would bring him recognition. Day after day he tried his hand at modeling until finally he had a subject that he felt was worthy of the Salon.

He had taken the idea for his subject from the pages of the Bible. All winter young Bartholdi worked on his project. He called it "Good Samaritan," and it showed an injured man stretched out on the ground being watched over by a Good Samaritan. After hours and hours of doing and re-doing Auguste was satisfied that he had done his best. He presented his statue to the Salon of 1853. Days passed. Weeks passed. Not one word was said by a single critic about his work.

Auguste loved Paris but it was good sometimes to leave work and disappointments and go to Alsace for a holiday among old friends. He enjoyed walking in his slow, measured way over the crooked, cobblestone streets of his native Colmar. In his mind's eye he would embellish this corner or that with imaginary statues of noble Alsaciens—

all, of course, to be executed and presented to the city without charge, by himself.

Even the chimes of the old church bell were a source of inspiration to him. One of his earliest works, which he titled "The Lord's Day," depicts his friends and neighbors on their way to church. Whenever he made a statue, he thought it fun to use the faces of real people.

It was while Auguste was visiting in Colmar that he decided to try again for recognition at the Salon. This time he chose for his subject a hero of Alsace, one of Napoleon's bravest generals, Jean Rapp. He convinced the town officials that a statue of General Rapp was just what was needed to enhance one of the town squares. Then he went back to Paris where he now had a studio of his own, and went to work.

He worked harder than he had ever worked before. Even though he worked long hours, Auguste never seemed to grow tired. Perhaps it was because he loved his work so much. Every few days his good friend, the well-known painter Jean Gérôme, stopped by to give Auguste encouragement and, now and then, a bit of help.

At last General Rapp was finished. Auguste's dark eyes fairly sparkled when he said: "Well, Gérôme, what do you think of my hero?" And Gérôme teasingly replied: "He is so big, the critics will have to notice him." Fortunately Auguste's new studio boasted an over-sized door so he didn't have to worry about getting General Rapp out.

"Anyway," went on Gérôme, "it's good enough for a celebration." Auguste brushed back his great mane of dark wavy hair, put on his jacket, and off they went to join their friends at a café nearby.

Among the group were several artists who specialized in painting pictures of the Orient. As usual the conversation was of far-away, fascinating places. Gérôme, who was older and who had already traveled in Egypt, talked excitedly of the grandeur of the Pyramids and the Sphinx. Just the thought of statuary of such huge proportions was enough to make Auguste tingle with excitement. Suddenly a brilliant thought came to him. "What do you say we all go to Egypt?"

What a celebration this turned out to be! Half the night they stayed up talking and planning! None of them had much money, but Gérôme, who knew his way around Egypt and who was delighted to go along, assured them that living was cheap on the Nile. So it was all settled. They would go, but not before General Rapp had been cast in bronze and had made his grand appearance at the Universal Exposition of 1855.

As it turned out, Auguste's statue was too big to go into the exhibition building. But Auguste was not one to give up easily. For a moment, he forgot all about Egypt. He spent hours, sometimes days, patiently waiting to see important members of the Salon Committee. Whether it was because of the charm of this persistent young sculptor, or whether the Committee felt General Rapp was a statue of unusual merit, is not known. In any event they solved the problem by allowing Bartholdi to display his statue in front of the exhibition building on the famed Champs Elysées. Auguste, now the envy of all the other exhibitors, went to Colmar to tell his friends of his good fortune, and to bid them goodbye before leaving for Egypt.

He had been in Colmar only a few days when a friend, who worked on a newspaper in Paris, sent him some clippings. General Rapp had been noticed by the critics! And their reactions were favorable!

This was the first time Auguste had received public recognition for his work. How happy he was. He was especially pleased because of Mama. Now maybe she would know in her heart that it was right for him to be an artist.

Auguste wanted so much to please his mother and to make her happy. Brother Charles, who seemed to care little for his mother's desires, pursued his own interests without so much as consulting her. So, more and more, Madame Bartholdi poured her affections on Auguste. When, some years later, in 1885, Charles died, it was Auguste who assumed responsibility for his brother's staggering debts.

Auguste with his mother

General Rapp was to remain on display on the Paris thoroughfare for all to see until Auguste returned from Egypt. The success Auguste had tasted with his "big" statue of Rapp made him more eager than ever to see the colossal monuments of Egypt. On his last day in Colmar, he went over to the Hotel of the Two Keys to bid good-bye to his good friend Chrétien Mugel, who was now the head chef there. "Some day, Chrétien, I am going to build the biggest statue in the whole world," vowed Auguste. "And when you do, I'll be there to cheer you," replied his good friend.

These were happy days indeed for Auguste. With Jean Gérôme as their guide, the four young artists took off for the land of the Nile. They may have lacked money, but they did have a wealth of enthusiasm and good humor.

At Damietta, near the mouth of the Nile, the five artists rented a small sailboat, called a "dahabeah." They put themselves at the mercy of the wind and began their six-hundred-mile trip up the Nile. First stop was to be the Pyramids near Cairo. A friend of Jean Gérôme had put a house at their disposal in Cairo where they could stay as long as they liked. Beyond that, they made no plans. They would stop and visit temples and monuments where and when they pleased. In between sightseeing they would hunt and fish.

Auguste was so excited at the prospect of actually seeing the great Pyramids that he insisted on telling and re-telling all the facts he had ever heard about these Wonders of the World. His companions threatened to throw him to the fish when, for the hundredth time, he said: "Do you realize that it took 100,000 men ten years just to make the pathway to transport the stone for the largest Pyramid and then another 100,000 men twenty years to complete the Pyramid itself?" Without giving anyone a chance to answer, he usually followed this with: "What a colossal nerve those ancient kings must have had to demand such labor just so they could have a showy tomb after they were dead!"

Or another time he would ask Jean Gérôme: "Is it true that the largest of the three great Pyramids covers eleven acres of ground and is 450 feet high?"

On the day that they actually tied their boat to shore and, in high spirits, boarded camels to make the short journey to the Pyramids, Auguste was strangely silent. In spite of all his knowledge, he was not quite prepared for the sight he saw.

Years later Auguste wrote of his visit: "We were filled with profound emotion in the presence of these colossal witnesses, centuries old, of a past that to us is almost infinite, at whose feet so many generations, so many million existences, so many human glories, have rolled in the dust."

Near the largest of the Pyramids Auguste gazed on the great Sphinx. He marveled at the fabulous monster with the head of a man and the body of a lion. "He has a look of utter content as he gazes out toward the Nile," noted Auguste.

During their stay in Cairo, Auguste visited the Pyramids many times. Several times he went in the company of Ferdinand de Lesseps, a fellow Frenchman who was in Egypt working on a plan for a gigantic canal. Bartholdi had great admiration for this veteran diplomat whose career had included important posts in Spain, Africa,

Switzerland, and Italy. De Lesseps knew all about Egypt, too. As a young man he had spent some time there with his father and later he had been French Consul in Cairo.

By the time they left Cairo Auguste already had visions of a new statue for Egypt. This one, he decided, would be twice as large as the Sphinx. He hadn't thought of a subject for such a colossal statue, but before the trip was over, he felt sure he would see a subject worthy of his grand idea. In fact he even spoke to De Lesseps about it, and received some encouragement. De Lesseps also urged Bartholdi to make another trip to Egypt for the inauguration of a grand canal at Suez, which, at this moment, was not even started.

Fun-filled days followed for the five. They were leisurely filling their notebooks with drawings, paintings, and sketches. The windowless, whitewashed houses stretched endlessly along the banks like so many building blocks; the water wheels pulled by oxen; the jaunty little donkeys with their loads of sugar cane; and even the choppy little fields of onions, beans, and wheat, were all subjects for an artist's notebook. One day they saw a moonfish blow himself up to the bursting point and collapse as he breathed out a weird message. They all spent the remainder of the day trying to preserve on paper their impressions of this live balloon.

They never tired of talking about the strange sights they saw. One visit to the caves filled with mummies of crocodiles provided conversation for days. "Where," they asked each other, "did these thousands and thousands of crocodiles come from?" They did not know the answer. Nor did anyone else.

Long before their journey came to an end, Auguste

had decided upon a subject for a statue for Egypt. He determined to make a tremendous statue of an Egyptian peasant. Everywhere he saw this peasant, known as a "fellah," at work—along the Nile dipping water by the bucketful to irrigate the meager crops, plowing in the mud, loading cotton. It was the fellah who carried the work load of Egypt. From the native clay, Auguste fashioned dozens of models. He told his companions: "Some day I will return to Egypt with a finished model of a statue of a fellah."

The influence of this trip to Egypt remained with Auguste all his life. To build colossal statuary became almost an obsession with him.

Weeks later when they were all back in Paris, they met at Jean Gérôme's studio. They did not laugh at Auguste when he said: "When I discover a subject grand enough, I will honor that subject by building the tallest statue in the world." In those weeks together along the Nile they had learned that once Auguste set his mind to something, he never gave up.

A friend of Jean Gérôme, a young American law student and artist named John La Farge, who had come to Paris to visit relatives, joined the group that evening. John La Farge and Auguste became good friends at once. John spoke excellent French and was anxious to learn all he could about French art. Auguste, on his part, never tired of hearing about America. They visited museums and theatres together.

John never ceased to marvel at the beauty of Paris. He enjoyed the luxury of the fancy carriages, the tree-lined avenues, the beautiful flowers in the many parks. Sometimes, in the evenings, he and Auguste would board a horse-drawn omnibus and head for an unusual section of Paris, high on a hill, known as Montmartre.

When they arrived at Montmartre, the two friends sometimes sat for hours talking and looking out over the city of Paris. Other times they would join artist friends in a quaint little café called the "Hopping Rabbit." Here, in one of its crowded, dimly lighted little rooms, they might sit next to the fat and aging Alexandre Dumas, who, if in a jovial mood, would himself go to the kitchen and prepare supper for the entire crowd. More than likely they would meet an up-and-coming young American artist by the name of James Abbott McNeill Whistler.

When John La Farge left for America, Auguste solemnly pledged to visit him one day.

For the moment, however, all thoughts of America were crowded from Auguste's mind. By a decree of Napoleon III, who by a vote of the people in 1851 had had his title of President replaced by Emperor, Bartholdi's statue of General Rapp was moved to Colmar and given an official inauguration. This was indeed a great day for Auguste! Important men of state, relatives, and friends all came to witness the ceremony. Madame Bartholdi, dressed in rustling black silk, shared honors with her twenty-two-year-old son. They sat with leading dignitaries in the first row on a special platform constructed for the occasion.

Encouraged by this success, Auguste entered a competition for a design for a monumental fountain for the city of Bordeaux. This he felt would give him a chance to show his ability as an architect as well as a sculptor. Here was a project to test his vast powers of imagination. After a hurried visit to Bordeaux, Auguste set to work.

Inauguration of the statue of General Rapp

He made dozens of sketches before he was completely satisfied. Then in his slow, methodical way he made detailed plans showing measurements and design for his fountain. On top of the fountain he had a majestic statue of Neptune and around the base were four elegant horses.

Thirty-five artists from all parts of France submitted entries. The judges eliminated first one project and then another. Finally there were only two projects left. Auguste's plan was one of them. He felt very honored to have received this much recognition. When several days later they told him he had won first prize, he was overjoyed. He could hardly wait to tell Ary Scheffer of his good fortune. The ailing Scheffer, who had been Auguste's guiding hand for so many years, said, a bit sadly perhaps: "You no longer need me. You can go your way alone now." The next year Auguste was deeply saddened by the death of this good friend. Ary Scheffer had given him confidence in himself and encouragement at the times when he needed it. He would never forget him.

The taste of success was a real inspiration to Auguste. No longer did his work go unnoticed by critics. His native Colmar asked him to do a statue of their famed Admiral Armand Joseph Bruat. Bartholdi turned all his energies to this project but even so it took him several years to complete it. The finished monument was a huge fountain with Admiral Bruat on a pedestal in the center surrounded by figures representing the countries where the Admiral had traveled.

On the faces of the figures representing these countries, Auguste tried very hard to portray the feelings of the masses of the people in each country. He must have succeeded in doing this. Many years later, when the great humanitarian Albert Schweitzer was just a boy, he visited Colmar and was so touched by the expression of sadness on the face of the powerful African that he did not rest until he went to Africa to help relieve the suffering there. Schweitzer himself has written of the great influence that Bartholdi's statue had on him.

The day the statue of Bruat was inaugurated was full of happy surprises for Auguste. Early in the morning honored guests began to arrive in Colmar. There were members of Bruat's family, as well as important government dignitaries from Paris, including a personal representative of the Emperor Napoleon III. Of course every one in Colmar turned out.

There was a parade and a band and speeches. Then it was time for Auguste to pull the cord that would unveil the statue. The crowd cheered until Auguste thought his heart would surely burst with pleasure. But that was not all. When the cheers died down the Emperor's representative came forward and said: "For your outstanding work on this statue, I have the honor to announce, in the name of the Emperor, your nomination as a Chevalier in the Legion of Honor." The delegate pinned the white enameled gold star badge on Auguste. How beautiful it looked on Auguste's fine black frockcoat.

Auguste choked a "thank you" and sat down beside his mother. It felt good to have her clasp his hand in hers. Only a few days before he had celebrated his thirtieth birthday, but right at this moment he felt like a little boy about to cry.

The events of the remainder of the day were but a blur to Auguste. Following the unveiling of the statue there was a musical program at the theatre in Auguste's honor. Choral groups from Colmar and nearby towns participated in the program. The final number, which was sung by the Colmar group, was a song written especially to honor Auguste. Auguste was like a man in a dream at the dinner that followed at the Hotel of the Two Keys. Even when his good friend Chrétien Mugel came out of the kitchen to admire the medal, Auguste, still unbelieving, said: "Do you think it's really mine?"

3

MONUMENT TO AMERICAN INDEPENDENCE

AUGUSTE was now a "man of two cities." He loved Paris. Here he was an artist among artists. It meant something to him to be able to breathe the same air and walk the same streets as eminent painters, sculptors, actors, poets, and writers. Paris provided the atmosphere a man needed to create a work of art.

Even his Paris house near the beautiful Luxembourg Gardens was just as he wanted it. After all, he had designed it himself. He was proud of his big, airy studio that looked onto a small walled garden filled with flowers, plants, and statuettes. He was perhaps the only artist in Paris whose house boasted one door for people and another giant door for his colossal statues.

Auguste loved Colmar too. The roots of his life were there. It pleased him to be a favorite son of Colmar. His mother no longer made the journeys back and forth to Paris, but spent most of her time in the fine old gabled house on Merchant's Street. It gave Auguste a warm feeling to know that she was there waiting to welcome him.

Since he had won first place for his Bordeaux design, Auguste was eager to enter another competition. This time it was a much grander project for a museum at Marseille. He made innumerable trips to Marseille, drew

Merchant's Street in Colmar

reams of sketches, and eventually came up with a most unusual plan. It was to be a double monument on the side of a hill to be joined together by a colonnade. In the middle of the colonnade was to be a dramatic cascade of water.

The city fathers of Marseille were deeply impressed and Auguste was confident he could make this the greatest work of his life. Instead, it became perhaps the greatest disappointment of his life. In the end, the officials decided Bartholdi was too much of a sculptor and not enough of an architect to entrust with such a vast project. They gave the work to another, who, to a great extent, utilized Auguste's plans. Auguste never gave up the battle for recognition of his part in the project. He carried his grievance to first one court and then another. He might have been appeased had his name merely appeared on a plaque as father of the idea. But when the completed work was dedicated and he was given no recognition at all, he simply could not rest. He felt a very great wrong had been done him. When, finally, years and courts later, he was awarded a sum of money for the damage he felt had been done him, he gave the money to charity.

The affair of Marseille left Bartholdi disappointed but certainly not discouraged. He was a persistent worker and worked long, regular hours. He liked to eat good food at regular mealtimes, and he liked to go to bed early every night.

Each year now the National Art Competition included something by Auguste Bartholdi. More and more heroes of Alsace were appearing in statues on the streets of Colmar. Relatives of departed ones began to look to Auguste for funeral monuments.

Important people sought the services of the young recipient of the Legion of Honor when they wanted, as was the fashion of the day, to have a replica of themselves in plaster. So it was that a prominent historian and law professor at the College of France thought of Auguste Bartholdi when he decided to have his "bust done." This man's name was Edouard de Laboulaye and even though he was years older than Auguste, the two became fast friends.

Perhaps this was because Laboulaye and Bartholdi were both admirers of all things American. Even though he had never been to America, Laboulaye knew more about the vast young country than many who lived there. He was the author of a three-volume history of the United States and had also written three volumes on Benjamin

Franklin. He had even written a book of fiction called *Paris in America* which had been translated into English and was widely sold in the United States. It was from this man that Auguste learned all about the Constitution of the United States. Also, from his discussions with Laboulaye, he became deeply concerned over the outcome of the Civil War. When Abraham Lincoln was shot, Bartholdi felt that he had lost a personal friend. He joined with forty thousand other French citizens in contributing toward a gold medal to be sent to Mrs. Lincoln as an expression of sympathy.

In presenting the medal to Mrs. Lincoln the Ambassador was instructed to say: "In this little box is the heart of France." The inscription on the medal said: "Dedicated by French democracy to Lincoln . . . honest

The gold medal which was presented to Abraham Lincoln's widow. The medal is now in the Manuscript Division, Library of Congress.

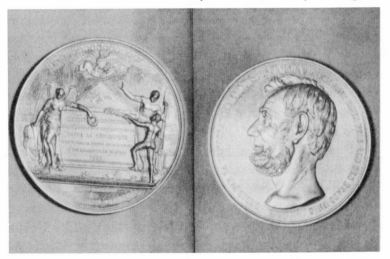

Edouard de Laboulaye

Lincoln who abolished slavery, re-established the Union and saved the Republic, without veiling the statue of liberty."

How strange it seems now that these symbolic words appeared even before the idea for a statue for America was conceived.

One evening, shortly after Lincoln's death, Auguste was invited to Laboulaye's home for dinner. Laboulaye lived in a beautiful house in a little village called Glatigny near the Palace of Versailles. Bartholdi looked forward to the occasion. Laboulaye was noted for serving good food. He also liked to surround himself with men of letters and

Auguste knew that the conversation would be as excellent as the dinner.

Bartholdi was not disappointed. Among the guests were Henri Martin, the noted French historian, several descendants of Lafayette, along with other notables. After dinner, when the guests were comfortably seated in the conservatory, the talk turned to America and to the important role France had played in America's struggle for independence. Auguste never tired of hearing how the brave young Lafayette, in the face of opposition from friends, relatives, and his country had gone off to America and offered his services to the Continental Congress saying: "I wish to serve you as a volunteer without pay."

Laboulaye firmly believed that Lafayette was honored in the United States as much as any American hero. "There will always be a bond between the United States and France," he said. "When hearts have beaten together something always remains, among nations as among individuals."

Laboulaye stood up. He was getting quite excited. The guests waited attentively. But none waited or listened more attentively than Auguste Bartholdi. Twenty years later he was still able to repeat Laboulaye's next words. "If a monument were ever built in America to celebrate the independence of the United States, it would be fitting that it be built by the united efforts of France and the United States, since they struggled together for American independence."

That night aboard the puffing little train that jerked from Versailles to Paris, Auguste took out his sketchbook and wrote down as much of the evening's conversation as he could remember. The word "monument" always

set his blood tingling. He was overwhelmed at the idea
of a monument grand enough to be the work of two
nations!

He thought about it all the way home. Inside his
house, he looked at the immense stuffed Alsacien stork
perched over the hall door. All of a sudden he was homesick for Colmar and his mother. She would understand his
excitement even though no one, not even Laboulaye, had
remotely hinted that Auguste be entrusted with the
making of such a monument.

Everywhere in Auguste's house were huge carved
wooden cabinets filled with miniature models of the many
statues he had done. He looked thoughtfully at them.
"What kind of statue did Laboulaye have in mind?"
mused Auguste. He carefully put his notes away and went
up to bed determined to ask Laboulaye about such a
monument the next time he saw him.

In a few days Laboulaye came to Auguste in great
excitement. He had decided to campaign in Alsace for a
seat in the House of Deputies and was going to Alsace
to meet people and to make speeches. Auguste was delighted. "I will go with you to Colmar," said Auguste,
"and introduce you to all my friends." The monument
of two nations was, for the moment, forgotten.

This time it was Edouard de Laboulaye's turn to be
impressed. When he entered the massive Renaissance door
into the spacious entryway of Auguste's Colmar home,
he was greeted by the most dignified and gracious lady
he had ever met. Auguste's mother was never happier
than when she could entertain a congenial group in her
home. She received her guests as beautifully as any lady
of court and presided with equal grace at the dining table.

This evening there was enough lively discussion of events literary and political to make Laboulaye realize that certainly all the brilliant minds of France did not reside in Paris. He gazed with admiration at the rows of portraits of distinguished ancestors that lined the walls.

Laboulaye lost the election, but he and Auguste became even closer friends. Laboulaye had real admiration for the bearded young Alsacien whose patriotic spirit made him eager to preserve in bronze the memory of all the favorite sons of Alsace.

Back in Paris, Auguste resumed work on the Professor's bust. Somehow the right moment to speak again of the monument of two nations did not come. The bust was finished. Laboulaye was pleased and Auguste exhibited it at the Salon.

Thoughts of America were pushed far into the background as Auguste heard more and more talk of the great canal that was nearing completion in Egypt. It gave him pleasure to know that the dreams of his good friend Ferdinand de Lesseps were being realized. Auguste remembered the invitation that had been given him, so many years ago in Egypt—half in fun, he knew—to attend the inauguration of the Canal.

As a matter of fact, Auguste had for some time been thinking of taking another trip to Egypt. His work clearly showed the influence of the study of colossal Egyptian art. For several years, he had won recognition at the Salon for statues with an Egyptian theme.

And Auguste still wanted to have a statue of his making erected in Egypt. "Why not design a statue grand enough to stand at Suez," thought Auguste. He ransacked his files and dusted off a huge portfolio of sketches labeled: "Trip with Jean Gérôme and Others." Fourteen years had elapsed since he had written that label. But, as he looked at the pictures, he recalled many of the events of this early trip. There was sketch after sketch of Egyptian peasants. Auguste had given them each a title: "Fellah dipping water from Nile for irrigating," "Fellah planting cotton," "Fellah woman making clay pitchers." He recalled boasting to his companions that he would return to Egypt with a statue of a fellah.

The more he thought about such a statue the more enthusiastic he became. Surely he could design a statue that would please the Khedive of Egypt. He wrote his friend De Lesseps and promptly received in reply an invitation to attend the inaugural ceremonies of the opening of the Suez Canal.

In fact, it seemed that half of Paris had received invitations to this historic event. It was well known that De Lessep's cousin, the beautiful Empress Eugénie, was making plans to attend.

Auguste was never happier than when he was working on some big project. When he wasn't at work in his studio, he was at the library reading everything he could find on Egyptian peasants. He wanted his statue to be a composite of all the toilers of Egypt.

How different this trip to Egypt from his first trip! This time he was a master instead of a student. Ferdinand de Lesseps greeted him warmly, introduced him to dozens of dignitaries, and saw that he was invited to all the important festivities. Handsome Auguste, with his dark wavy hair, his neat beard, and his flashing dark eyes, had a flair for graciousness that won him favor everywhere.

He realized that until the affair of the inauguration of

the canal was over, no one would have time even to glance at his model for a proposed statue. In the meantime, he enjoyed Egypt. This time he had a comfortable ride in a carriage to the Pyramids over the road that had been specially built for the visit of the Empress.

He met Charles Longfellow, son of the American poet Henry Wadsworth Longfellow, and, with the help of De Lesseps, the two of them managed an invitation to ride aboard the French war steamer *L'Aigle* as she sailed from Port Said to Suez leading the inaugural procession. The most distinguished guest aboard this ship was the Empress Eugénie. Later the young men attended a magnificent exhibition of Arab horsemanship, and in the evening they were among the six thousand guests at a great ball given by the Khedive in a palace built especially for the occasion.

When the fanfare of the inauguration died down, De Lesseps saw to it that Auguste had an opportunity to present his sketches and model for his Suez statue to important government officials. They admired it. "They were so obviously impressed," said Auguste, "that they didn't even bother to discuss costs." Like the thousands who had come from all over the world, Auguste had witnessed the lavish entertainment of the Egyptian government. It never occurred to him to think that such a government might be so short of money that they couldn't afford a statue no matter how badly they might want it. Auguste himself seldom worried about costs. "If Egypt wants the statue," thought Auguste, "perhaps I can persuade Empress Eugénie to make them a present of it."

It was suggested by some that the statue might serve

the purpose of a lighthouse at Suez. If De Lesseps had any doubts about the sincerity of the encouragement that had been given his friend, he didn't mention them. He had something of greater importance on his mind. Within a few days, he was going to be married. Auguste was pleased to be among the few close friends who attended the ceremony.

All in all, Auguste felt his second trip to Egypt had been a huge success. Now he was anxious to get back to Paris and his studio. However, so sure was he of executing his Suez statue, that he took a roundabout way home by way of the Italian Lakes so he could examine an Italian statue that was being used as a lighthouse.

Auguste returned to Paris full of new, grand ideas. He gained an audience with the Empress who promised to give consideration to his lighthouse as a French gesture of friendliness to Egypt. Then he turned his thoughts to his entry for the Salon of 1870. This second trip to Egypt had added to his enthusiasm for colossal monuments. He was determined to choose for his next statue a subject that would be worthy of the grand scale on which he liked to work. After years of study, he was well aware of the peculiar laws and difficulties involved in the creation of colossal statuary. "The size of the statue," he often said, "must be in keeping with the magnitude of the idea."

He finally chose a subject to his liking from the pages of ancient French history. He decided to create a statue of a two-thousand-year-old Gallic chief named Vercingetorix. History records that this brave chief led the rebellion which started the Gallic War and that he fought a mighty battle against Caesar in the central part of France. When his model of the heroic war lord on a fine horse was shown at the Salon, Bartholdi was overjoyed at the acclaim it received from critics.

He had high hopes that the city fathers of Clermont-Ferrand would be impressed enough to want a colossal statue of this ancient hero whose birthplace was near their city. Bartholdi made a trip to this charming city on a hill at the foot of a volcanic range of mountains. "What a setting for Vercingetorix," thought Bartholdi. Clermont-Ferrand thought so too. Auguste was ready to go to work in earnest on this project. Then, all of a sudden, his happy world went topsyturvy.

On July 19, 1870, France declared war on Prussia. Auguste's first thoughts were of his mother. Once he had heard the crushing news he could not rest even for a moment. All thoughts of a statue were forgotten. Auguste bade a hasty goodbye to his friends in Clermont-Ferrand and left that very day for Colmar.

All his life, Auguste had been hearing about liberty. Never once had he felt anything but free. Now he was about to learn what it means to lose this liberty.

4

FRANCE AT WAR

AUGUSTE sat in the crowded railway station. He was
worried and confused. For two days he had moved with a
wave of pushing, shoving Frenchmen. The entire popu-
lation of France seemed to be trying to board the same
train. Everywhere he saw soldiers. Now Auguste was only
a few miles from Colmar. One more miserable train ride
and he would be there.

By this time he was frantic enough to push and shove
too. He was among the aggressive few who elbowed their
way onto the next train. Auguste ran all the way from the
station to Merchant's Street. He didn't so much as give
Admiral Bruat a passing glance as he sped by.

There was his mother waiting for him, calm and beautiful as always. Even though troops were camping in the
nearby fields and even though the government had given
orders for the peasants to harvest their crops as quickly as
possible, Auguste's mother had no fear but that France
would crush the enemy in a very few days.

When Auguste saw that his mother was in no danger
and that there was no panic in Colmar, he decided to go
to Paris and offer his services to his country. Thanks to
his mother, his old self-confidence had returned. He knew
what to expect now at the railway stations and on the

Bartholdi in the uniform of
the National Guard

trains. In a way, he even enjoyed the excitement and hub-
bub of his trip to Paris.

Bartholdi joined the National Guard of the Seine and
was promptly made a major and given a position on the
staff. In this capacity, he was able to follow closely the
events of the war at the frontier. Paris was jubilant over
the news of victories reported from the Emperor's headquarters at Metz.

Little did Auguste realize that the reported triumphs
were but wishful thoughts of the harried Napoleon.
Finally Napoleon was in such a difficult position that he

could no longer withhold the true state of affairs from Paris. "Hasten preparations for the defense of Paris," was Napoleon's message.

When Auguste heard this he could not help but worry about his mother. He knew Napoleon must be in serious difficulties to send such a message. So Auguste asked to be transferred to a military unit nearer Colmar. He was granted three months' leave of absence from his post in Paris to organize the National Guard in the vicinity of Colmar.

By the time Auguste put his affairs in order preparatory to leaving, Paris was seriously preparing for her "defense." Droves of cattle passed all day along the city boulevards to be pastured in the lovely parks of Paris. Wagonloads of supplies of all kinds were being stored in public buildings, even in elegant theatres. Auguste was deeply saddened by what he saw. For the first time he realized the seriousness of the situation. He was more anxious than ever to get to Colmar.

This time Auguste was in uniform and under military orders so he had no difficulty in gaining transportation. His mother, as before, was calm even in the face of rumors of masses of enemy troops nearby. Bartholdi's orders were to organize the National Guard and join with the "regulars." He soon discovered there were no regulars in the area to join.

However, he immediately went about the task of organizing his fellow Alsaciens into a home guard. On September 2, 1870, Colmar was shocked by the news that Napoleon had been taken prisoner at the border town of Sedan. Eighty thousand French soldiers were taken captive at the Sedan surrender.

Auguste worked day and night trying to get guns and equipment for his men. He was beginning to understand what Laboulaye meant when he spoke of the American "struggle" for independence. The "struggle" in France had only just begun. On the afternoon of September 13th, Auguste received orders to organize his men to take arms outside the city. By midnight all of Colmar was in a state of tumult. A company of snipers that had been stationed on a little bridge just outside Colmar returned to the city in the chill small hours of the morning with word of the approach of 5,000 enemy soldiers. Auguste could hear the distant roar of cannon.

The men all gathered at the City Hall. They looked to Auguste for leadership. The defenses of the neighboring city of Strasburg were already in ruins. "What should they do?" thought Auguste. He could see the folly of the home guard trying to defend the city against the onslaught of 5,000 well-trained, well-equipped soldiers. He knew there was only one right choice to make. It was a bitter pill—surrender to the enemy.

By 10:30 that morning, the Prussians began filing in. They wore helmets with spikes on top and each carried a fixed bayonet. They each had a sabre on one side and a huge horse-pistol two feet long on the other. They ordered the French to turn in all their weapons and go about their daily affairs in a peaceful manner.

Auguste had scarcely arrived home when seventeen Prussian soldiers tramped in to the Bartholdis' beautiful courtyard. Auguste thought surely they had come to get him. He and his mother watched them from an upstairs window.

Describing the episode later to a friend, Auguste said:

"At first, I couldn't figure out what the soldiers were up to. They took off their knapsacks, stacked their guns, put their helmets on top of their bayonets, and spread their greatcoats out on the ground. Then they sat down on their coats and proceeded to take off their boots and socks. We decided all they wanted to do was rest awhile."

What a jolt Auguste and his mother had later in the day when a spokesman for the group asked for mattresses and bedding and informed them that they were moving into the first floor!

The enemy soldiers showed no signs of moving from the Bartholdi house. Auguste had some satisfaction though in seeing the great respect they had for the dignified lady of the house.

Auguste's mother knew he was unhappy in Colmar. Much as he would have liked to have him with her, she urged him to go. Her birthday was September 29th. Auguste had never been away from his mother on her birthday. This year would be no exception. They even invited a few close friends for the occasion and for an hour or so pretended there were no uninvited guests on the floor below. While the celebration may have lacked the gayety of former years, there was a friendly warmth about the gathering that cheered Auguste when he thought about it many times later after he had become one of an army of nomad soldiers.

After the birthday celebration Auguste bade his mother a hasty goodbye and walked out of the city gates. Little did he realize, as he turned to give his beloved Colmar a sad farewell glance, that the next time he entered her gates he would be entering Germany.

The next few weeks were a gruesome nightmare for

Auguste. Everywhere there were soldiers, cannon, horses —all on the move. No one seemed to know where to go or what to do. The roads were blocked by wagons loaded with provisions and clothing. Worst of all, there was no news of what was happening in Paris. Weeks before, the fifty-one gates of Paris had been closed and the railroad entrances walled up. Rumors of battles won and lost filled the countryside.

One day Auguste heard a rumor that was so fantastic he was sure no one could have made it up. He heard that his former commanding officer, a fiery orator by the name of Léon Gambetta, had flown out of Paris and across the German lines in a balloon. Rumor had it that Gambetta had been made Minister of War and had gone to the City of Tours to organize the defense of France.

Bartholdi made his way as quickly as he could to Tours. There he found Gambetta and placed himself at his service. The balloon story, Auguste discovered, was even more fantastic than the rumor. He found that a pigeon postal service had been established. Now mail was being carried quite regularly across enemy lines from Paris to the provinces by balloons. These balloons also brought carrier pigeons so that the people in the provinces could answer their mail. On a dark night, from a high point in Montmartre, Gambetta had flown out of be-sieged Paris and had brought with him the first carrier pigeon.

The one-eyed Gambetta was short, dark, stout and had a decided lack of social graces, but when he spoke of France, it was with a heart-stirring eloquence that in-spired his colleagues to superhuman efforts. Auguste was no exception. He was given the task of obtaining supplies.

Gambetta leaving from Montmartre in a balloon

At that moment there was no money in Gambetta's treasury, nothing in the arsenal, and but a few volunteers in the army. At the end of six weeks the treasury was full, two great armies were organized and supplied with artillery, horses, and food. Once, in his search for supplies, Bartholdi went to Bordeaux to meet a ship from America loaded with arms and munitions. He stayed long enough to talk with the ship's men because, he said: "I had always felt a sympathetic curiosity toward America and a lively desire to know the country."

Auguste continued to have the job of obtaining supplies, but in addition he was now serving as liaison officer between the army commanded by Gambetta at Tours and the army commanded by the famous Italian fighter Giuseppe Garibaldi, with headquarters at Dole. With Garibaldi were men of all nationalities. Bartholdi was beginning to understand why Lafayette had fought in America. Liberty was worth fighting for, even if it wasn't your own.

Auguste and the white-bearded Garibaldi often traveled together inspecting troops and hunting needed supplies. After his trip to Bordeaux, Auguste spoke to Garibaldi about his desire to see America. Bartholdi was surprised to learn that years before, when Garibaldi was in disfavor in his native Italy, he had gone to America where he had worked in a candle factory. He spoke with deep feeling about the kindness of the Americans. Bartholdi was more than ever determined to get to America some day.

That winter Bartholdi suffered great hardships. Often the rheumatic sixty-year-old Garibaldi and his men fought knee-deep in snow. But never once did Auguste forget he was an artist. He always carried a pencil and sketchbook with him. In the trenches he often cheered his fellow soldiers by drawing funny pictures. He gave many of the sketches to his companions, but some of them he saved. When the war was over he planned to have them printed in a book.

Garibaldi's men were not the only soldiers who were suffering. Throughout France it was the same story. All news received was bad news. Surrender after surrender was reported. The only cheering note was the story of the little town of Belfort on the Swiss border that was miraculously holding off the enemy. So when the word came that an armistice had been signed, Auguste was not surprised, but he was sad and disappointed.

When the terms of the armistice were made known, Bartholdi simply could not believe that his dear Alsace, all except brave Belfort, along with the northern part of the Province of Lorraine, had been ceded to Germany. Shortly before a friend had delivered to him a letter from his mother. She had assured him of her good health and urged Auguste not to worry about her. He was anxious to go to her, but at the moment Alsace was closed to Frenchmen.

So he went to Paris instead. How good it was to be in his studio again after an absence of nine months. Even with her broken trees, her littered streets, and her boarded shops, Paris was a beautiful sight to Auguste. He hastened from one friend's house to another. One friend burst into tears when he saw Auguste. When Auguste inquired: "Do I look that sad?" his friend answered: "I weep tears of joy because you are alive. I thought you were dead."

Auguste was very anxious to see his friend Edouard de Laboulaye. He wanted to talk to him about America. During the past bitter months Auguste had thought a great deal about his "sister country." He had witnessed the joy of his comrades when needed supplies reached the battlefields from America. The idea of a monument to American independence had a personal meaning for him now.

For a moment, when Bartholdi first entered Laboulaye's home in Glatigny, he thought he had been transported back to 1865. There gathered in the conservatory he saw his good friends Henri Martin and Oscar Lafayette. The same as before, the talk was of America.

This time it was Auguste who took the lead in the conversation. He spoke about the coming celebration in the United States of the one hundredth anniversary of their independence. "Might it not be fitting that we give the Americans a gift on this great occasion?" suggested Auguste. His friends all thought this a very good idea. "But what kind of gift?" they asked.

This was Auguste's chance. "I think we should give the Americans a statue," and he paused long enough to catch his breath, " a statue of liberty." He looked around him. His friends were delighted. " It would have to be a grand statue," one suggested. "Yes," agreed Auguste. "I propose to make a statue that can be seen from the shores of America to the shores of France."

Laboulaye spoke up then and said to Auguste: "Go to see that country. You will study it, you will bring back to us your impressions. Propose to our friends over there to make with us a monument, a common work in remembrance of the ancient friendship of France and the United

States. We will take up a subscription in France. If you find a happy idea, a plan that will excite public enthusiasm, we are convinced that it will be successful on both continents, and we will do a work that will have a far-reaching moral effect."

Now Auguste was more impatient than ever to see his mother. She always gave him encouragement, no matter what the project. He knew he could not put into words his feelings about America. But Auguste felt sure his mother would understand and give him her blessing.

Even though there was red tape for Auguste to cut before he had permission to enter Colmar, he felt more cheerful than he had for months. Laboulaye had promised to give him letters of introduction to friends in America. Auguste's artist friends in Paris were almost as excited as he about the proposed trip. They gave him a real send-off when he boarded the train for Colmar. Auguste was actually lighthearted.

Not until he reached the border of Alsace did his feelings change. For a few moments, he had tried to forget the war. Suddenly he was face to face with a grim reminder in the form of a new signboard. "Des Alsass," it said. This was only the beginning.

The quaint weatherbeaten Colmar sign on the station that for so many years had meant home to Bartholdi was replaced by a huge board. No mistaking its sharp letters. "KOLMAR," it said. Before he stepped off the train he was reminded that the people in Kolmar spoke German.

No doubt now in Auguste's mind about the meaning of liberty. Even the stores had strange-sounding names. Auguste felt humiliation for the dear little crooked cobblestone streets. What had they done to be deprived of their names? Auguste hurried to Merchant's Street. By now, he was prepared for a change. But he was hardly prepared for "Schadelgasse." His poor mother! How could she bear it? Skull Street!

After one look at the familiar rows of portraits of proud Bartholdis and Beyssers on the walls Auguste knew he never should have had doubts about his mother. There was no defeat in her attitude as she stood tall and regal at the top of the stairs waiting to greet Auguste.

Auguste was distressed to find Prussian officers billeted in his old room. The officers, however, were extremely well-behaved and even admired the stately French lady who simply ignored their presence and spoke to them only when absolutely necessary, but always in excellent German.

The wise woman knew that Auguste would not be able to curb his feelings. Madame Bartholdi watched her son daily express his bitterness with a spatula and clay. He shut himself in his little studio, drew the curtains against unfriendly eyes, and began to work. He put all his feeling into the three figures which he named "The Curse of Alsace." There was deep sadness in the statue of a woman who knelt beside the body of a dead soldier. The soldier was still grasping his flag in his hands. A child, its face innocent and hopeful, stood beside the poor widow.

It was perhaps at this time also that Auguste made the sketch for a monument for the Colmarians who had lost their lives during the war. This starkly dramatic monument represents a tomb, the top stone of which is slightly raised as if by the shoulder of a man, and out from under it extends a bony arm with a shriveled hand that reaches for a sword that lays just beyond its grasp.

If Madame Bartholdi had any fears and doubts about Auguste's proposed trip across the sea, she kept them well hidden. In fact she urged him to hasten with his plans for the voyage. Auguste wrote at once to Laboulaye to remind him of the promised letters of introduction. "Above all," wrote Auguste, "I hope to realize my project of a monument in honor of American independence."

Funeral monument designed by Bartholdi to honor the National Guardsmen who died in combat

5

BARTHOLDI VISITS THE UNITED STATES

JUNE 8, 1871 was a day to remember! This was the day Auguste boarded the *S. S. Pereire* bound for America. Even though the long voyage across the Atlantic was still ahead, Auguste felt he was well on his way.

It had already been two weeks since he had parted from his mother. He was glad now she had not gone to the railway station with him. He liked to think about her right there at home. The short journey to the port of Le Havre had turned out to be so difficult that several times Auguste couldn't help wondering if he were doing the right thing to go to America. Now that he was actually on board all his doubts vanished. The late trains, the days of waiting in stations for trains that didn't arrive at all, the crowds, the disappointment over the *Pereire's* delay in sailing, and the miserable wait in Le Havre—all this was forgotten. Auguste was not even thinking of France as he stood on deck and watched the fading shoreline. His thoughts were of America and the monument.

Auguste did not have a single sketch on paper for such a monument. He didn't even have an idea of what a Statue of Liberty for America should look like. All he knew was that more than anything in the whole world he wanted to make such a statue.

Auguste's feelings about liberty were very real ones. His own war experiences had probably taught him the most. He had learned a great deal about American liberty from his association with Scheffer and Laboulaye and his friendship with La Farge and young Longfellow. His knowledge was not all hearsay, either. He had read volumes on American history.

His luggage contained a neat pile of folders and guidebooks on travel in the United States. Auguste had every intention of seeing a large part of the country before he returned to France. It never occurred to him to worry because he did not have a design for his statue. He was sure before he reached the shores of America he would have his idea.

The first day of the voyage was calm and pleasant. For the first time in months Auguste was able to relax. He got out his sketchbook and began to think of a design for his Statue of Liberty. Of one fact he was sure. To do justice to the grand idea of freedom in America, nothing short of a colossal statue would do. But how does one portray liberty? Auguste recalled various paintings and statues he had seen labeled "liberty." They were all gruesome and violent. That wasn't at all what he had in mind. He thought of the poetic words Laboulaye had written: "Liberty is the mother of a family that watches over the cradle of her children, that protects consciences, that multiplies schools . . . Liberty is the sister of Justice and of Mercy, mother of Equality, Abundance, and Peace."

"That's the kind of liberty enjoyed by Americans," thought Auguste. "I must design a statue that will portray these thoughts."

For two days, the sun shone and the sea was calm. Auguste sat in his deck chair and began to sketch. At the end of the second day, he tossed all his sketches into the sea. "I will make a fresh start tomorrow," he said.

It was several days before he was able to do any more drawing. In the night, the winds began to blow, and by morning there was a real gale. The *Pereire* bobbed every which way in the frothing sea. Auguste wondered if they were even headed in the right direction.

Auguste finally gave up waiting for the angry sea to subside. He shut himself in his cabin, tried to ignore the groans of the poor distressed ship, and concentrated on his design. On the twelfth day at sea, the Captain announced they would reach their destination the next morning. Bartholdi collected the drawings that littered his cabin. Wearily he looked at each. Not one suited him. Finally he gathered them all together and went up on deck. He looked gloomily at the cloudy sky. Then, one by one, he threw his sketches into the billowing water.

He had a great feeling of relief when the last of the lot disappeared. "Now," he said again, "I can make a fresh start." That night the moon shone and the sea was calm again. As Auguste looked out over the peaceful water he was haunted by the memory of a sight he had seen many years before. It was of the young girl who had held a torch high in her hands as she jumped over a barricade.

"Why do I think of her?" wondered Auguste as he went off to bed.

Auguste slept so peacefully and so soundly that he overslept. New York City was already in view by the time he arrived on deck. The day was breathtakingly beautiful. "I saw the New World in a pearly radiance," Auguste afterwards said. He gazed at the vast expanse of shore, at the puffing, whistling vessels of all sizes that swarmed about the *Periere*. His eyes wandered to a tiny egg-shaped island. An American on board told him it was Bedloe's Island.

Toward one end of the island Auguste saw the outline of a huge eleven-pointed star. From his American companion he learned that this fort had been built years before as part of a series of fortifications to guard the harbor. When Auguste looked more closely, he could see some of the old cannons that still surrounded the fort.

As Auguste continued to gaze at this little island that seemed to guard the gateway to America, a strangely happy feeling came over him and he made a vow: "In this very place shall be raised the Statue of Liberty."

He hurried below, got his sketchbook and his water-

An early map of Bedloe's Island

Sketch of "Liberty Enlightening the World" by Bartholdi

colors. In a few minutes he had completed his design. At last he had a picture of liberty! Liberty was a tall and proud lady with one arm bearing a torch raised high to the sky and the other grasping a tablet bearing the date July 4, 1776. Around her head was a golden crown of rays.

Auguste was so pleased with his lady that he decided to give her a name. "I will call her 'Liberty Enlightening the World,' " he said.

When he got off the ship, Bartholdi was so busy trying to see everything at once that he barely missed getting caught between a wagonload of "heaven knows what all" and a carriage with spider-like wheels. Everywhere people seemed to be madly rushing. Even the buildings appeared to have been put up in a great hurry. Here was one eight stories high and right next to it a haphazard shanty. Merchants, street peddlers, and auctioneers crowded alongside the bumpy cobblestone streets selling their wares.

"I am truly in a new world," thought Auguste. He was still in the same happy mood when he knocked on the studio door of his friend John La Farge. It had been sixteen years since Auguste had met John in Paris. They had kept up a lively correspondence, and Auguste felt John was his one friend in America.

John did not disappoint him. He welcomed Auguste with warmth and sincerity. He was most enthusiastic over the idea of the statue and urged Auguste to begin at once on a clay model. Since La Farge spent a good deal of his time at his home in Newport, Rhode Island, he invited Bartholdi to make use of his New York studio. He laughingly warned Auguste to take care because his studio had

only one door, and, he said, "it is quite the normal size."
Auguste promised that even though he fully intended his
"Liberty Enlightening the World" to be the biggest statue
in the world, he would start off by making a tiny model.

Once the model was finished, Auguste was pleased
with it. He was eager to show off his lady of liberty and
to get the reactions of Americans. It was the right time,
he decided, to make use of his letters of introduction.

Auguste remembered that Laboulaye had urged him
to pay an early visit to Mary Louise Booth. Miss Booth
was a great admirer of Laboulaye and had translated
many of his writings into English. She was editor of a
leading fashion magazine. Auguste made an appointment
to see her and was pleasantly surprised to be greeted in
perfect French.

She listened intently to Auguste's story of the meetings
at Laboulaye's home and of the hope for a Statue of Liberty. She admired the little model and suggested that Auguste see President Grant about the project.

Pleased and encouraged, Auguste made arrangements
at once to make the short trip to Long Branch, New Jer-
sey, to see President Grant. The President greeted Bartholdi on the steps of the simple, two-and-a-half story
frame box that served as the summer White House.
"What a contrast to the Palace at Versailles," thought
Auguste.

They had just gotten settled on the "sea side" of the
enclosed porch that surrounded the house when Bartholdi
was startled by the loud report of a cannon. Grant laughed
and hastened to explain that it was only a friendly salute
from a passing ship. President Grant listened attentively
to Auguste's plan and commented most favorably on the

President Grant's summer home, Long Branch, N. J.

model and the watercolor of the proposed statue. While he didn't make any commitments, Auguste was more than pleased with his reception of the plan.

After his visit with Grant, Auguste decided to go to Washington to see what suggestions Laboulaye's good friend Senator Charles Sumner might have. On his way to Washington he stopped off in Philadelphia to meet another friend of Laboulaye, Colonel John W. Forney, publisher of the Philadelphia *Press*. Colonel Forney held an important post in the planning of the celebration of the one hundredth anniversary of American independence to be held in Philadelphia in 1876. He introduced Auguste to a number of influential men in Philadelphia. They all admired "Liberty Enlightening the World." A wealthy member of a Philadelphia club that claimed Laboulaye as an honorary member purchased Laboulaye's bust from

Bartholdi as a gift for the club. Colonel Forney discussed the possibility of Auguste's making an ornate bronze fountain for the coming Exposition.

Auguste spent the Fourth of July in Washington, D. C. He had curious, mixed feelings about the capital city of America. Her big wide avenues, laid out like the spokes of a wheel, with the Capitol building for a hub, faintly reminded Auguste of Paris. But it was a Paris stripped of all her beautiful trees, parks, buildings, and statues. Here, many of the avenues were not paved at all. By the time Auguste reached the dusty grounds around the partially finished Washington monument, he was so hot and tired he took more interest in outwitting the flies than in the holiday speeches.

Later as he crossed Lafayette Square on his way to Senator Sumner's house he thought of his own green Luxembourg Gardens. What a welcome surprise was in store for the homesick Frenchman! The walls of the Senator's home were literally covered with choice paintings, engravings, and photographs, many of them scenes of France. The entire place was crowded with fine French furniture and tapestries.

In among it all was a chaos of books, manuscripts, and newspapers. Auguste glanced around for a place to sit down and Sumner, faultlessly neat and well dressed, stooped from his great height and brushed a pile of books from a chair. Sumner knew France well through travel as well as study. He plied Auguste with questions about the war, about Laboulaye, about politics. When Auguste finally got a chance to tell Sumner why he had come to America, the Senator immediately made plans for Auguste to meet influential men in Washington.

Auguste felt he was making real headway. He wrote Laboulaye: "Thanks to your name, I have had the most cordial reception; you are here not merely popular but honored and beloved to an extent which I cannot describe."

Auguste had not yet used half his letters of introduction but he decided to accept the La Farges' kind invitation to spend a few days with them at Newport. Among the other guests at Newport were several young architects. One was Richard Hunt, who said he liked to design pedestals. When Auguste, jokingly, perhaps, asked him: "How would you like to design a pedestal for the largest statue in the world?" Hunt promptly replied: "I accept the job with pleasure."

Another of the guests was H. H. Richardson. Auguste liked Richardson immediately. Perhaps this was because Richardson had lived for some time in Paris and had worked in the offices of several French architects. When he invited Bartholdi to Boston to look over plans he was doing for a new church there, Bartholdi readily accepted.

In Boston, Auguste found what he termed "a bit of the Old World." Here no one seemed to be in quite such a hurry. Here he dined with men of science and letters. He was delighted when Henry Wadsworth Longfellow invited him to his summer home in Nahant, a few miles from Boston. Bartholdi had looked forward to meeting the great poet ever since he had met Charles Longfellow at Suez. He was more than a little excited when he boarded a boat for the little resort village by the sea. When he arrived, white-haired, white-whiskered Longfellow received him as if he had always known him. "When I left him," said Bartholdi, "he pressed my hand as if he wished electrically to convey the pressure to his friends in France. He charged me to express to them all his enthusiasm for their plans."

Auguste was quite surprised to learn that no one he met had made a trip across America. This, despite the fact that many of his new friends had toured Europe extensively. Rumors of "a long, hard trip" didn't in the least dampen his enthusiasm and toward the end of August he left from the new Grand Central Depot in New York on a pilgrimage of America.

Auguste arrived in Chicago a few weeks before Mrs. O'Leary's cow kicked over the lantern that started a fire that all but destroyed the city. He was amazed to find a city of 300,000 people so far inland. He marveled at her great factories and at the tremendous number of other buildings. "Already," he wrote to his mother, "there are 126 churches and 100 newspapers."

Bartholdi's next stop was Omaha, Nebraska. Then he began the tedious journey across miles and miles of prairie where for days one saw nothing but a few sod houses, burnt countryside with gray grass, and dried up strings for branches on the trees. Once the train was held up for hours waiting for a large herd of buffalo to pass. Sometimes, from the train window, Auguste caught sight of the jagged, rutty trails of the determined pioneers who had been the first to break through the wilderness.

As they approached Utah, Auguste was impressed by the masses of red sandstone that rose abruptly in the midst of level plains. He made innumerable sketches of these. At Promontory Point, Utah, he saw the spot where only two years before the Central Pacific and the Union

Train to the West stopped by buffalo

Pacific had joined "tracks" after a great race. Bartholdi saw the gold and silver spikes that had been driven into the final ties on May 10, 1869.

As he got farther west, boom towns became more and more frequent. Mostly they consisted of a few shacks, sometimes a tent or two, and rough, hardy looking men. Salt Lake City was like an oasis in the midst of this wild wilderness. Here he saw the great Mormon Temple that had a seating capacity of 8,000. He paid a visit to Brigham Young and wrote afterwards to his mother in amazement about a man who had sixteen wives and forty-nine children.

The guidebooks spoke glowingly of the beauty of the giant redwoods of California. Even though it was a day's trip from a railroad junction by stagecoach to the interior of the forest, Auguste decided to make the venture. There were moments that day when he wondered if he had not carried his pilgrimage of America too far. "What a road! What dust! What a stagecoach." Most of the time Auguste had to brace himself with both his hands and his feet to keep from being thrown out of his seat. All the while his eyes were blurred and his skin grazed by the sand and grit from the rutty road.

It was almost nightfall when they reached the hotel located in a little clearing on the edge of the open forest. Even though this hotel was like many Bartholdi had seen along the way—hardly more than a roughly constructed shanty—it was a most welcome sight. After dinner, Auguste joined a group for a walk into the moonlit forest. The sight he saw repaid him many times over for his miserable ride. Who could help but be impressed by those magnificent giants? They ranged in age from four hundred years to six hundred years. Some of them were 350 feet high and 20 feet around.

Perhaps it was after this jaunt that Auguste wrote to Laboulaye: "Everything in America is big." In speaking about American food, he said: "Here, even the peas are big."

Auguste felt a real sense of accomplishment when he reached the Pacific. "It is truly a grand country." he said. He spent days in San Francisco, talking to everyone he met about his monument, recording with brush and paint scenes of this fabulous hodgepodge of a city. In fact in every city Auguste visited he found Americans who expressed great interest in his "Liberty Enlightening the World." From San Francisco, he wrote to Laboulaye: "The ground is well prepared; only the spark will have to be provided by a manifestation on the part of France."

It was well into Fall when Auguste began his return trip across the continent. From Missouri he wrote: "We cross for some time some superb forests. Autumn is giving them some ravishing color." At St. Louis he marveled at the floating palaces that steamed up and down the Mississippi.

He spent several days in Pittsburgh, Pennsylvania, visiting iron, steel, glass, and other manufacturing plants. He described it as a city where hundreds of furnaces poured forth dense volumes of black smoke.

By the time Auguste returned to the nation's capital, Congress was in session. Senator Sumner welcomed him as an old friend. He saw to it that Bartholdi had a chance to discuss his statue with many influential political figures who had been away from Washington when he visited there in the summer.

When Auguste left New York, he felt confident of the success of his project. His experiences of the past months had given him an awareness of the freedom enjoyed by the people of this great country. He stood on deck and watched Bedloe's Island fade from view. "Yes," he said, "I am sure that it is right that on that island should rise 'Liberty Enlightening the World.' "

6

A FRENCH PURSE FOR MISS LIBERTY

WHILE Auguste had been touring America, civil war had been raging in Paris. He returned to find his beloved city badly burned and full of open war wounds. The beautiful Palace of the Tuilleries was completely gone; his cherished Louvre museum was partially burned. Everywhere he saw blackened shells that once were houses.

He was grateful that his own house on Vavin Street had been spared. Eager as he was to get on with his Statue of Liberty, he realized that the people of Paris were too concerned with their own affairs to care about a gift to celebrate American independence. There was still plenty of time, he thought. After all, the celebration was not until 1876. He would wait for a more opportune moment.

In the meantime, he set about finishing several projects he had been commissioned to do. He had purposely delayed going to Colmar. He did not look forward to seeing his native city in the hands of the conquerors. His mother, keenly aware of his reluctance to return, had assured him that she was all right.

The little town of Belfort that had heroically stood siege for seventy-three days during the Franco-Prussian War decided to erect a monument to commemorate this defense. They opened a competition among artists for a design for such a monument and Auguste decided to enter. He drew many sketches before he had a plan that he felt was worthy of the heroes of Belfort. The design he finally submitted was of a colossal lion. Belfort was pleased and Auguste set to work on the project. He went several times to Belfort to choose a site for his lion. He finally decided to place it on a red rock on a hill that overlooks the town. Back in Paris, he began work on a clay model of this great statue. At first he thought he should have a live model, but after a few tries at having a so-called tame theatre lion "sit" for him, he gave up the idea. He did, however, spend many hours watching live lions before he completed his first model. After he finished it, many people came to Auguste's studio to admire this great beast. The lion was represented as wounded, but still capable of fighting. He was half lying, half standing, with an expression of rage and mighty defiance on his majestic face. An arrow lay at his feet.

Other commitments kept Auguste from completing the Lion of Belfort and it was not until 1879 that this statue was unveiled with much fanfare and a great torchlight parade in Belfort.

About this time the French government decided to present the city of New York with a bronze statue of Lafayette in recognition of the help given her during the war. Bartholdi was given the commission to do this work to which he promptly turned all his energies. He spent many weary hours searching in national files for portraits of Lafayette as a young man. He wanted to portray the dashing Lafayette in his earliest days of fame when he first put himself at the service of Washington.

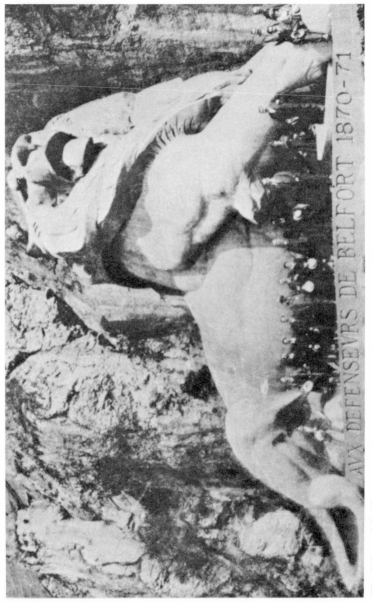

The Lion of Belfort

His plaster model, which was on display at the Salon of 1873, won great acclaim. He portrayed Lafayette in the act of taking a step toward Washington, and holding out his left hand as if to offer his services. His right hand pressed a sword to his breast. Perhaps Auguste had tried to capture the moment when Washington told him the American troops he would have to lead were badly drilled and worse equipped. To which Lafayette replied: "I have come hither not to criticize but to learn."

Despite the fact that Auguste was busy, he managed to find time to keep up a steady correspondence with many of his American friends. One day Auguste received a letter from his architect friend H. H. Richardson that made him very happy. When Auguste was in Boston he had admired Richardson's plans for a huge church with a square tower. "Now it seems," wrote Richardson, "that the artist who had planned to design the frieze around the Romanesque tower will be unable to do so." He continued: "Would you possibly have time to do this work?" As a special inducement, he mentioned that John La Farge had consented to paint the murals inside the church.

Auguste was delighted. He loved America and it made him very proud to have his art appear in this country. He went to work on the frieze with his usual energy, applying all his great powers of imagination. His finished design was of four groups of colossal sculptured figures representing Baptism, Communion, Marriage, and Death. For the four corners of the tower, to lean out just below the eaves, Auguste designed four angels, each with a golden trumpet. He gave the faces on some of the figures in the frieze the likeness of men he especially admired.

Lincoln, Longfellow, Emerson, Hawthorne, Garibaldi, and Sumner are among those who today look down from the heights of this church on Brattle Street in Boston.

While Auguste was putting the finishing touches on this elaborate design, Charles Sumner paid him a surprise visit. Sumner was no stranger to Paris, but it gave Auguste pleasure to browse with him among the bookstalls along the River Seine, and to help him in his avid search for more paintings and bric-a-brac for his museum-like collection.

After Sumner's visit, Auguste began to give serious thought to the fountain he had promised to do for the Centennial Celebration in Philadelphia. His thoughts, too, turned more and more to "Liberty Enlightening the World." Already his studio was a bit cluttered with a variety of clay models of Miss Liberty. When the opportune moment came to present the project to the people of France, Auguste wanted to be well prepared.

Long ago he had decided that his mother's fine noble face had the character and classical beauty he was so anxious to portray in his statue. He still, however, was searching for a model who would stand patiently with shoulders erect and arm upraised until he could produce a Statue of Liberty that completely satisfied his critical eye.

It is at this time in Auguste's life that an event took place which caused him perhaps both the greatest sadness, as well as the greatest joy he would ever know. It happened on the occasion of the wedding of a friend that he attended in a fine old Gothic church in the city of Nancy, capital of ancient Lorraine.

After the wedding ceremony Auguste stood outside

Bartholdi at the time he started work on the Statue of Liberty.

the church waiting for the bride and groom to make their grand exit. Suddenly he noticed a very beautiful, plainly dressed girl standing in the background with a group of curious townspeople. She had lovely, graceful arms. Her shoulders were straight and she held her proud head high.

At once Bartholdi thought: "At last, there is my model for my Statue of Liberty. But who is she? How can I meet her?"

He inquired discreetly of several of the guests. It was Madame Navarre, the fashionable modiste of Nancy, who had designed the bride's wedding gown, who gave Bartholdi the young girl's identity. "She is but a poor dressmaker's assistant in my shop."

Madame Navarre was more than surprised when Auguste insisted upon being introduced to the girl. For Auguste, it was a storybook romance. For the first time in his forty years, he fell in love.

Her name was Jeanne-Emilie Baheux de Puysieux. She was the daughter of a fine old aristocratic family of Nancy. Because of her father's severe financial losses, she had been forced to go to work. She fell in love with Auguste and with the Statue of Liberty, too. She moved to Paris and stayed with a friend so as to be near Auguste and to pose for his great American statue whenever he needed her.

Auguste loved her and wanted to marry her, but somehow he could not bring himself to tell his dignified mother of his romance with a seamstress's helper. Each time his mother came to Paris to visit him, he thought he would surely have the courage to tell her. But he never did. Kind Jeanne-Emilie was so much in love with him she did not press him. Perhaps if she had been more insistent, he might at least have introduced her to his mother. "Some day," she assured him, "you will find a happy moment to tell your mother."

Auguste was very anxious to complete a perfect model of his Statue of Liberty to show to John W. Forney, the

Philadelphian who would soon be in France on a goodwill tour for the coming Centennial Celebration. Forney especially wanted to see Auguste's plans for his Philadelphia fountain.

The model of the huge cast-iron fountain was all but completed when Mr. Forney called at Bartholdi's studio. He was so impressed by all its detail that he wrote at length about it for his Philadelphia newspaper, mentioning the cupids, the "nymphs of exquisite form," and the three beasts that were to spit water into the lower part of the fountain.

He looked with interest at Lafayette, at the frieze for the Boston church, and was fascinated by Belfort's lion. When Auguste showed him his finished model of "Liberty Enlightening the World," Forney promptly asked: "You will have that statue ready for the Centennial, won't you?"

Auguste simply could not say "No," and he didn't dare say "Yes." He was well aware of the tremendous cost of a statue such as he had in mind. Right now, not one cent of money was available for this purpose. So Auguste answered: "I will make every effort to have it ready."

Mr. Forney left for a few days in London and Auguste decided that this was the right time to ask the people of France to contribute to a gift for America. He called on Laboulaye and in a few days a meeting of important Frenchmen and Americans in Paris was scheduled to take place at Bartholdi's studio to discuss a campaign to raise funds. An urgent message to London brought Mr. Forney back for the meeting. The most important American to attend this meeting was Elihu B. Washburne, American

Minister to France. He had a special place in the hearts of the French because he was the only foreign envoy who had stayed in Paris during the terrible siege following the war in 1871.

As Auguste welcomed the distinguished gathering to his studio, he could not help but remember an evening ten years before when many of these same gentlemen—Lafayette, De Noailles, Martin, Rochambeau—had gathered at Laboulaye's home for dinner. He wondered how many of them remembered what Laboulaye had said that evening: "If a monument were ever built in America to celebrate the independence of the United States, it would be fitting that it be built by the united efforts of France and the United States, since they struggled together for American independence."

Auguste opened the discussion by telling the group about his trip to America and about the favorable reactions he had received to "Liberty Enlightening the World." Then a number of the other men who had long been familiar with the project spoke in its behalf. After much discussion, all agreed that the monument should "be executed in common by the two peoples, associated in this fraternal work as they were formerly in founding independence." It was Martin, the historian who said: "We shall make a gift of the statue to our friends in America; they will unite with us to provide the cost of the execution and of the erection of the monument which will serve as a pedestal."

Thus the Franco-American Union was born to make plans and secure funds for the successful completion of "Liberty Enlightening the World." Laboulaye was named president of the organization.

A public appeal for funds was made immediately. "Let each bring his mite," said the daily newspapers. "The smallest subscriptions will be well received. Let the number of subscriptions express the sentiments of France." Notices of the formation of the Franco-American Union were also sent to the American newspapers in the hope that a similar committee would be formed there to raise funds to build the pedestal.

The French people were most receptive to Laboulaye's pleas for funds. Money started coming in immediately. The Committe even rented an office. Already Auguste was besieged by visitors who wanted to have a look at his two-and-a-half-foot model of a colossal monument for America.

A "birthday" celebration for Miss Liberty was scheduled for November 6, 1875. Two hundred distinguished French and American men were invited to the formal dinner at the Louvre Hotel. The dining room was resplendent in red, white, and blue decorations. There were portraits of Washington, Franklin, Lafayette, Rochambeau, Lincoln, and Grant. The guests included representatives of the press, government officials, men of arts and letters, including Alexandre Dumas. They sat at three tables which were arranged to form a large horseshoe. The head table was decorated with a model of the Statue of Liberty. At the open end of the horseshoe was a beautifully colored transparency showing the statue as it would appear on Bedloe's Island.

During the dinner, telegrams were sent at the same instant to President Grant of the United States and to President McMahon of France, conveying an expression of the feeling of the gathering toward this great work.

After midnight, when the last guests had gone home, Bartholdi gathered together the subscription blanks that had been distributed during the course of the dinner. In one short evening a substantial amount—enough to make Auguste confident he would be able to complete the work —had been pledged.

A few weeks later the Franco-American Union sponsored a public fête at the Palace of Industry as part of their fund-raising campaign. Directly in front of the main door of the Palace was a striking painting of the statue. Bartholdi stood in a corner and watched the Parisians as they admired his "Liberty Enlightening the World." He could not help but think of the first time he had ever had an exhibit in this building. What a disappointment he had suffered when his "Good Samaritan" received no public acclaim. That was twenty years ago. But his thoughts were pleasantly interrupted by a gentleman who praised Miss Liberty and who offered to donate a large share of the material needed for the building of the statue.

The members of the Franco-American Union were tireless in their efforts to spread the word about a proposed gift to America. Money began coming in from all over France. Big and little merchants, industries, city councils, and even children were sending in their contributions.

Auguste had been aware all along that it would be impossible to build the biggest statue in the world in his own studio. Now it was time for him to find a place where he could begin the work. But, even the largest workshop in Paris was not large enough! This did not in the least dampen Auguste's spirits. Nothing could stop him now. He had waited too long for this opportunity to be discouraged at this point. He simply set about convincing the owners, Gaget and Gauthier, to enlarge their shop to make room for Miss Liberty.

Auguste knew, too, that he would have to have many helpers. Those who admired his model of the statue thought of it only in terms of a "work of art." In reality, its construction was an architectural and engineering feat. No one man could possibly execute such a work by himself. So, while a staff of secretaries in the offices of the Franco-American Union were busy sending out 14,000 subscription blanks to make it easier for the people of France to donate their money, Auguste was interviewing workmen.

Gaget, one of the owners of the shop, agreed to render engineering services. Auguste was pleased that his aging friend, the sculptor Simon, whom he had admired for many years, was willing to help. Auguste also hired two foremen and a modeler. His statue was going to require a steel frame. Auguste knew a man who was being acclaimed all over France for his wonderful steel bridges. His name was Gustave Eiffel and he expressed a willingness to try his hand at building a steel skeleton for Miss Liberty. Perhaps it was the success he eventually achieved with the Statue of Liberty that later inspired him to build a landmark for France, his famed Eiffel Tower.

Auguste was also spending long hours drawing up work schedules. Would it be possible for him to finish the statue in time for the Centennial Celebration in America? Laboulaye was pressing him for complete estimates of the cost. Auguste, always optimistically underestimating rather than overestimating, was constantly having to revise his figures.

Madame Bartholdi came to Paris and was worried because, for the first time in his life, Auguste was not eating and sleeping regularly. She complained that Miss Liberty was taking every moment of her son's time. Only when his presence was required in Liberty's behalf, did Auguste take time from his planning for a social evening. One such occasion, planned by the Union, was a grand benefit musical at the lavish new Opera House. When they entered the exquisitely decorated foyer of the Opera, Madame Bartholdi and her son were escorted up the marble staircase to an especially reserved velvet and gilt-lined box. Bartholdi had invited one of the members of the Union, Senator Bozerian, to join him at the Opera. "You will understand later the special reason for my invitation," he had told the Senator. When Senator Bozerian entered Bartholdi's box, he could not conceal his amazement when he looked at Madame Bartholdi. "She is the statue of 'Liberty Enlightening the World,'" he exclaimed. Auguste, pleased, pressed his hand and said: "Yes, she is the Statue of Liberty. She is also my mother."

The curtain went up. On the backdrop was a dramatic painting of the statue in its setting in the New World. When the applause died down, Laboulaye, looking frail and picturesque, mounted the rostrum and opened his talk with: "See how I love America? At my great age I mount the platform for her."

He was eloquent in his plea for financial aid for Miss Liberty. In closing he delighted the audience by saying: "We are told that when Lafayette returned to France from America all women wished to embrace him. I am no general of twenty-five, much less a victorious general, so I'll just ask you kindly to embrace my cause."

The highlight of the evening's program came when the composer of the opera *Faust,* Charles Gounod, conducted the cantata entitled "Liberty Enlightening the World" which he had written especially for this occasion. A young lady dressed in a flowing Grecian costume, not unlike Miss Liberty's own, and holding the American flag, recited the words which had been set to Gounod's music by Emile Guiard. Her voice, sweet and clear above the music, rang out:

> *I have triumphed—I am one hundred years old—I am called*
> *Liberty—this is but a name, that is too little.*
> *The world has made, wishing me strong and beautiful,*
> *My body of bronze and my soul of fire. . . .*

A few days later Auguste went to the station to see

The opening bars of Gounod's song, *Liberty Enlightening the World* his mother off to Colmar. For the first time, Madame Bartholdi could not understand her son. The gigantic workshop he needed was all ready and he had plenty of workmen available to begin work the minute he gave the signal. True, the money was not coming in quite rapidly enough to meet his rising estimates, but there was no doubt now that the dream he had had for so many years was to be a reality. Why, then, did she detect such a note of sadness in him? "Was he still grieving so much for Alsace?" she wondered as she waved to him from the train.

No, it was not of Alsace Auguste was thinking. It was of Jeanne-Emilie. His mother had come and gone again and still he had not told her about his Jeanne-Emilie.

7

AN ARM FOR AMERICA

ON A crisp cold morning in the winter of 1875, when most of Paris was asleep, Bartholdi walked alone toward the newly enlarged workshops of Gaget and Gauthier. So deep was he in his thoughts that he didn't even glance at the Arch of Triumph as he turned off the Etoile to Number 25, Chazelles Street. He wanted to get there in time to arrange all his drawings and his charts before any of his workmen arrived.

Auguste had worked out a method for building a statue that would not only be the biggest in the world, but would be one that he hoped would stand forever. Today he would try to explain these plans to his workers. The men, he knew, were anxious to get started on the gigantic statue. Then, too, the Franco-American Committee was putting pressure on Auguste to complete the statue in time for the Centennial Celebration in America. Auguste had stubbornly refused to start work on the actual statue until he was absolutely certain that every detail of construction had been planned and that his working model was right in every respect.

In his own studio, he had made dozens of clay models before he finally had one that satisfied his critical eyes. Jeanne-Emilie had stood for hours with her weight resting on her left foot as if she were taking a step forward. In the completed statue, a shackle, which Liberty symbolically has broken, lies in front of her right foot. The shackle chain disappears beneath the draperies of Liberty's dress and reappears in front of her left foot. The end link is modeled to appear broken.

Other times Jeanne-Emilie stood patiently with her right arm upraised so that Auguste could fashion a perfect Miss Liberty holding aloft her torch to symbolize the light of liberty.

When Auguste was not actually working on his clay model, he was busy with research and calculations. He even consulted United States weather records in making plans for a statue that would withstand the fury of the most powerful hurricane.

"Surely I have not overlooked a single detail," thought Auguste as he entered the big, silent workshop. He carefully spread his drawings on a huge, crudely constructed table. At one end of the table stood the four-foot model of the statue. Bartholdi called this his "model of the studio." This was the one for which Jeanne-Emilie had posed so patiently.

Auguste glanced at his pile of papers on the table. Who could know the time and thought that had gone into those tedious plans? First he had had to decide: "What material must I use to construct a statue of such giant proportions?" Stone, he knew, would never do. It was much too heavy. Even if he used small stones and put them together, the cracks would show. Then he thought about bronze. But bronze was very expensive and also very heavy. After all, this statue had to be shipped across the ocean. It must be made of something that was both durable and light in weight.

Bartholdi thought of the various huge statues throughout the world. He remembered one very unusual one that was neither stone nor bronze. It was the statue of St. Carlo Borromeo in Italy, and it was made of copper. Certainly it was durable because Borromeo had been standing on the shores of Lake Maggiore since 1697.

Auguste smiled to himself. He had been so pleased when he finally made the decision to make his Liberty of copper. Even though all the work of building the statue was still ahead of him, Bartholdi had studied and made his plans so carefully that he was sure once he explained the process to the workmen the work would proceed rapidly.

The sculptor Simon and the modeler Beron were the first to arrive. They were quickly followed by Bergeret, supervisor of copper, and members of his crew, and by a large group of carpenters headed by Parent. They gathered around the four-foot model, eager to begin. First of all, explained Bartholdi, a plaster statue twice the size of the original one had to be made. Then a working model thirty-six feet tall, or one-fourth the size of the finished statue, would be made.

"When our thirty-six foot plaster working model has been made perfect in every detail," said Bartholdi, "then we will begin the task of making the full-sized model in plaster." Of course none of the men had ever heard of a statue as tall as Bartholdi had in mind. No such statue had ever been built. But they listened attentively as Bartholdi explained his plan. They had every confidence in him and were proud of the part they were to play in this great undertaking.

According to Bartholdi's plans the huge study model, which was to stand in the center of the workshop when it was completed, was to be divided, by means of carefully drawn lines, into many sections. Then each section would be reproduced separately and enlarged again four times to the size of the final statue.

It was the job of the carpenters to make a framework of laths for each section, over which would be spread a thick coating of plaster. Then, using an intricate system of dots and guidelines marked on the study model, the sculptor and the modeler were to copy into the pile of plaster every tiny feature of the model section. "This means," said Bartholdi, "putting some three hundred major marks on our study model besides twelve hundred smaller guidemarks. In order to be sure we are being absolutely accurate, we will measure each mark three times on both models."

At this point, Bergeret, who had been hired to supervise the copper work, spoke up: "I'm quite puzzled. I thought the statue was to be made of copper."

"So it is," replied Bartholdi. "When a section of the statue has been made absolutely perfect in plaster, then we will make a wooden mold over the plaster cast." Bergeret was still puzzled. "Then," continued Bartholdi, "when these wooden molds have been made to fit every projection, depression, and curve of the plaster, the copper workers will begin."

"I understand it all now," said Bergeret. "We are to hammer the thin sheets of copper into the wooden molds, and when we take the copper out of the mold, then we

will have an exact replica in copper of the plaster model.
A very difficult task, to say the least."

"When all the copper pieces have been made," went on
Bartholdi, "we will fasten them with rivets to a steel
frame that Gustave Eiffel is designing."

Bergeret was quite pleased with the role he was to
play in Miss Liberty's construction. "In other words," he
said, "we in the shop are to make Liberty's skin while
Eiffel puts up her skeleton in the yard."

"Already," thought Auguste, "my fine workmen are
beginning to love the Statue of Liberty. They do not seem
to mind the hard work ahead of us."

The Committee was so pleased that actual construction on the statue had begun that they doubled their efforts to raise funds. They still hoped the finished statue
could be shipped to America the following summer in time
for the Centennial Celebration. But Auguste and his men
knew now that this was impossible. Laboulaye, President
of the Franco-American Union, finally reluctantly con-
ceded that the statue could not possibly be ready in 1876.
The Committee then decided to ship the upraised arm
holding the torch to Philadelphia for display at the International Centennial Exhibition.

Twenty men worked ten hours a day to complete the
twenty-one sections that made up the right arm and hand
holding the torch. Bartholdi was everywhere at once in
the workshop—checking and rechecking the tiniest details. "If the statue is made exactly right," said Bartholdi,
"it will stand forever."

Despite all this work, Auguste managed to find time
to finish and ship his statue of Lafayette to New York
as well as his fountain to Philadelphia. He also entered

At work on Liberty's arm

several small statues and some watercolors he had done in California in the art competition at the Philadelphia celebration.

Auguste was selected by the French government to be one of the official delegates of France to the Centennial. The delegation, headed by the tall, handsome Marquis de Rochambeau, grandson of the famous French commander at Yorktown, was due to sail from Le Havre on the *SS Amérique* on May 5, 1876. They were to serve as members of an international jury to judge works of art at the exposition. President Grant was to officially open the exhibition on May 10th.

By early spring Bartholdi began to doubt whether Liberty's arm would be ready in time for the Philadelphia opening. All day, and far into the night, the workshop resounded with the din of hammering and sawing and the banging of mallets on copper. Even so, when Bartholdi left Paris with the delegation, the arm was far from finished. Now the best he could hope for was that it could be shipped in time to make an appearance in Philadelphia before the exhibition closed in the fall.

Aboard ship, Bartholdi amused himself and other passengers by drawing cartoons of the members of the jury. Louis Simonin, who was also a member of the Franco-American Union, wrote gay bits of verse to accompany each of Bartholdi's sketches. Later Bartholdi and Simonin published their work in a book called *Album du Bord* and gave all the profits from the sale of the book to the Franco-American Union.

Auguste was greeted in Philadelphia by his cousin, Amédée Bartholdi, who was now the French Minister to the United States. Together they toured the exhibits at the

Fair. Auguste was pleased with the fine location of his fountain between the machinery hall and the main building. Everyone was sure to see it. They had to pass the fountain to get to the amazing exhibit of an invention by a man named Alexander Graham Bell. This invention was, of course, the telephone.

It was still several days before the reception for the international jury was to be held so Auguste and Amedee made a quick trip to New York to check on the statue of Lafayette. Bartholdi was greatly disappointed to find Lafayette still crated and in a warehouse because there was no money for the pedestal. He quickly called a meeting of a group of French-American citizens and arranged for the French newspaper in New York to begin a subscription to raise funds for the pedestal. He also spent an evening with his good friend John La Farge who happened to be working in his New York City studio.

Auguste rushed back to Philadelphia for the reception and for a round of important dinners and parties. His watercolors of California and the statues he had put on exhibit were being noticed with favor. One of the statues, that of a fresh young Alsacien vineyard worker with his little dog, remained in America. It is now at Drexel Institute in Philadelphia. Students at Drexel claim it gives them good luck to rub the little worker's big toe before taking examinations. Over the years the bronze of the statue has mellowed to a soft, dull finish. All but the good-luck big toe. It is rubbed bright and shiny.

Bartholdi was very anxious for Liberty's arm to arrive, but the latest word from Paris indicated it could arrive no sooner than August. Well, Bartholdi had suffered disappointments before. He would make the best of the situation. He arranged for the arm to make its grand appearance as part of the "New York Day" celebration which was to be held on September 21st.

Auguste was disappointed to discover that no effort was being made in America to raise funds for the pedestal for the statue. He did not blame the Americans. Rather, he felt that somehow, in spite of all his efforts, he had not created sufficient interest.

He wrote to Laboulaye: "My courage will never fail. Your name personifies the work, and I esteem it too highly not to exert all my strength. It is like a standard to me— a little heavy at times, but as I have the honor to carry it, I shall not falter."

On the Fourth of July, while his friends were boating, picnicking, or swimming, Bartholdi went to New York for a most unusual celebration. He felt this day, July 4, 1876—just one hundred years after the signing of the Declaration of Independence—was a memorable time to make his first trip to Bedloe's Island. He knew a lot more about the little island now than when he had first seen it from the ship on that beautiful day in 1871 and had been inspired to make his sketch of Liberty. The island had gotten its name, he had learned, from an early owner, a wealthy merchant and shipowner by the name of Isaac Bedloo.* After Bedloo's death the island passed from one hand to another and was used for various purposes—quarantine, hospital, pest house. It was finally ceded to the United States government in 1800 and shortly after that the Star Fort was constructed as part

---

* This was his name, and the original name of the island, which later became Bedlow's Island and, finally, Bedloe's Island.

of America's coastal defenses. During the Civil War the fort was used for storage of guns and ammunition and as a recruiting station.

As Bartholdi boarded the funny old tugboat, along with a small party of contractors and engineers, he was probably the only one who took notice of the tugboat's name—the *Washington*. "It's a good omen," thought Auguste. They reached the island and scrambled over the decaying wharf. The engineers immediately got out their equipment and began to survey the area. They were half blinded by the blazing July sun. They weren't the least bit enthusiastic about the work. After all, so far, there had been no official word from the Capitol about a Statue of Liberty.

Auguste was unaware of the heat as he stumbled along the top of the old sea wall, past the rusty old guns to the entrance to the fort. "It's just like a castle in a story book," said Auguste when he crossed the drawbridge over the moat and entered the massive iron doors into the yard of the fort. A great feeling of peace came over him. Later when he wrote of his visit to the island, he said: "The statue was born for this place which inspired its conception. May God be pleased to bless my efforts and my work and to crown it with the success, the duration, and the moral influence which it ought to have."

On the way back Auguste suggested to his companions that it would be fitting to change the name of the little island to "Liberty Island." One of the men grumbled that since the island had been called Bedloe's since about 1664 he could see no reason to change the name now.

On the evening of the Fourth, Bartholdi joined thousands of New Yorkers to watch a gaudy torchlight parade and to view the windows and fronts of the various buildings that had been decorated for the occasion. The winning window displayed an immense panorama of the New York coastline with a vividly lighted Statue of Liberty in the foreground.

The mob surged in front of the window and cheered and applauded. "Will these same people tomorrow be willing to donate even a little bit toward Miss Liberty's pedestal?" wondered Auguste. It had been a big day. Auguste was tired, weary, and lonesome. It was late, but he decided to go to John La Farge's studio, just on the chance he might be there. Bartholdi was in luck. Both John and his wife, Margaret, who had come to town for a party, were there.

Suddenly Auguste felt like talking about Jeanne-Emilie. When he finished telling his good friends about the muddled, hopeless situation he seemed to be in so far as his mother and Jeanne-Emilie were concerned, sweet Margaret La Farge came forth with a startling solution to his romantic problems. "Why not send for Jeanne-Emilie to come to America?" she suggested. "You will be married at our house and return to France with your bride. When your mother sees how happy you are, she will love Jeanne-Emilie as you do."

They talked far into the night. Auguste went off to his hotel with a lighter heart than he had had for many months. It was dawn when he finished writing Jeanne-Emilie.

While he waited impatiently for her to reply, he worked on the campaign for the pedestal fund for his

Lafayette statue. When her letter arrived, Bartholdi was so happy he rushed to Newport to share the good news with Margaret and John.

Yes, Jeanne-Emilie would come. She had gratefully accepted Margaret's invitation to stay with them and she thought December a fine time for the wedding.

After that, everything seemed to go right for Auguste. Miss Liberty's arm arrived in Philadelphia in twenty-one crates on August 12th and workmen began immediately the task of assembling it on the exhibition grounds between the pavilions of a New York newspaper and a travel agency. When Bartholdi saw the work well under way, he took two bronze casts of his Statue of Liberty to Washington to deposit them in the United States Patent Office according to the law of the day. (These models were later disposed of by the Patent Office and one of them was obtained by the New York Trust Company. It now stands in the lobby of their main office in New York City.) At the same time, Auguste completed the sale of his Philadelphia fountain to the city of Washington where it may be seen today in the Botanical Gardens a few steps from our nation's Capitol.

Good news came from New York, too. Lafayette's pedestal had been completed and dedication ceremonies for the statue were set for September 6th.

What a celebration that was! Bartholdi was amazed at the tremendous crowd that turned out to witness the parade and to cheer him as he raised the American flag in which the statue had been veiled. He was more than pleased with the pedestal which had been presented by the French citizens of New York City. His Lafayette stood upon the fragment of a boat as if he were stepping

Statue of Lafayette by Bartholdi in Union Square, New York
City

from its deck. He thought the inscription on the pedestal
a well-chosen one: "As soon as I heard of American independence my heart was enlisted—1776."

Wealthy Americans, who were either art fanciers or
civic-minded, began to make inquiries about the sculptor
Bartholdi and his Statue of Liberty. More and more Bar-

tholdi was in demand to speak in Liberty's behalf before distinguished gatherings. His prestige was further enhanced when the Centennial Fine Arts Awards were made public and Bartholdi's statues as well as his California watercolors won recognition.

On New York Day, crowds began to arrive in Philadelphia at six in the morning. By the end of the day

Liberty's arm on display at the Philadelphia Exposition

Jeanne-Emilie

125,000 had been there and had seen Miss Liberty's gleaming copper arm and torch. So great was the interest in the arm that Auguste arranged for it to be shipped to New York for display in Madison Square when the Fair was over.

When Jeanne-Emilie arrived, she marveled at the change in Auguste. "He is so much gayer and more confident of the future," she confided to Margaret. "It is you who have given him that confidence," replied Margaret, who was charmed by the French girl's sweet and friendly manner.

Jeanne-Emilie and Auguste were married quietly on December 15, 1876 at the Newport home of the La

Farges with only the minister, John and Margaret, and their eight-year-old daughter in attendance. "Never in the world," said Auguste to John, "did anyone have two such fine friends as I have in you and Margaret."

The La Farge household overflowed with the joy and happiness of Jeanne-Emilie and Auguste. To Jeanne-Emilie it was like a storybook Christmas. She delighted her hosts by her enthusiasm for anything and everything American. She had never before eaten popcorn and she loved it. She and Auguste spent hours in front of the fireplace popping corn in a wire popper over the open flame.

On the day after New Years Bartholdi went to New York to confer with a group of prominent Americans about the pedestal for the Statue of Liberty. These men—lawyers, bankers, publishers, wealthy merchants—wanted the statue for America. This time they did more than just praise the project. They organized a committee to superintend the raising of funds for the pedestal. William H. Evarts, a well-known lawyer who later became Secretary of State, was chosen chairman and Richard Butler, merchant and art fancier, was made secretary. They were businesslike and confident of the success of the enterprise.

Bartholdi felt he had done all he could in the United States on behalf of "Liberty Enlightening the World." It was up to the Americans now. His place was in Paris in the workshops of Gaget and Gauthier.

8

MISS LIBERTY
TOWERS OVER THE HOUSETOPS

MADAME Bartholdi came to Paris to be on hand to welcome her son and her daughter-in-law. She had missed Auguste while he was in America. Besides she wanted to pass judgment on his bride. Fortunately for Auguste, his mother liked Jeanne-Emilie immediately, and the two became good friends.

Auguste had been back in Paris only a short time when he received some news from the Pedestal Fund Committee in America that made him very happy. "Liberty Enlightening the World" had at last been given an official blessing by the United States government. Quite fittingly, on George Washington's birthday, Congress passed a joint resolution:

> That the President of the United States be and he is hereby authorized and directed to accept the Colossal Statue of Liberty Enlightening the World when presented by citizens of the French Republic, and to designate and set apart for the erection thereof a suitable site upon either Governor's or Bedloe's Island, in the harbor of New York; and upon the completion thereof shall cause the same to be inaugurated with such ceremonies as will serve to testify the gratitude of our people for this expressive and

felicitous memorial of the sympathy of our sister republic; and he is hereby authorized to cause suitable regulations to be made for its future maintenance as a beacon, and for the permanent care and preservation thereof as a monument of art, and of the continual good will of the great nation which aided in our struggle for freedom.

A letter from the secretary of the committee, Richard Butler, assured Auguste that plans were being made to circulate subscription papers throughout the United States to give all citizens a chance to participate in the building of the pedestal.

With such fine encouragement from America and with the happy state of affairs between the two people he loved most in the world, Bartholdi was able to give his undivided attention to the building of his statue. In the great barnlike workshed, amid piles of boards, sawdust, and chunks of plaster, Auguste supervised the final touches on Liberty's noble head. A newspaper reporter who visited the shop described this work vividly:

A number of pigmies of our species, crawling about the inside of what appeared to be a vast cauldron used in the sugar-refining trade, were understood to be really at work on the crown of her head. A smaller cauldron, on which two little fellows were busy in a corner, was the tip of her classic nose . . . . The Lilliputians reached her back hair by means of ladders running from stage to stage of a high scaffolding.

Bartholdi wanted to have the gleaming head, neck, and shoulders of "my daughter Liberty," as he often affectionately referred to the statue, ready for display at the Paris World Fair of 1878. Some days as many as fifty

men were at work on the head and as many visitors came
to gaze in astonishment. It was a weird sight to watch
the men, all caked with white plaster, as they crawled
around on the lumber skeleton of a section of the giant
woman with their rulers and their compasses. Bartholdi,
dressed in a dusty old smock, was always on hand. He
was never too busy checking minute details to answer
visitors' questions.

Once in a while, for an especially distinguished guest,
he would dress in high fashion and personally escort the
visitor through the maze of frames and wires. One such
visitor was General Grant, who spent a few days in Paris
in the Fall of 1877 when he was making a trip around
the world. A crowd of newspaper reporters followed Gen-

General Grant visits the workshop in Paris

eral Grant and the Marquis de Rochambeau to the shop.
Grant was amazed at what he saw. Here in the middle of
piles of rubble was the gleaming head of a giant beauty
that stared with eyes two-and-a-half feet wide and smiled
with lips as long as the General's walking stick. "You
know," said Grant more to himself than anyone else,
"until now I never really believed the young man who
rocked on my front porch so many years ago." No one
except Auguste knew what he meant.

"I wish every American could visit your shop," said
Grant as he said good-bye. "I wish they could too."
thought Auguste; "then maybe they would want to help
build a pedestal for Miss Liberty."

Miss Liberty herself was having money troubles. Auguste had never received a single franc for his work, nor
did he ask for payment. With him, he said: "Liberty is
the labor of love." The workmen, though, had to be paid.
In order to speed the work so that the head and shoulders
could appear at the World's Fair, Auguste had hired
many extra men, and money was going out as rapidly as
the committee could collect it.

In spite of all the extra work, the head was not quite
ready for public display when the Fair opened on May 1,
1878. Auguste refused to allow the head to be moved until
every tiny detail was absolutely perfect. Bergeret and his
copper workers were busy all day long with tiny mallets
gently tapping a spot on Liberty's nose, her cheek, or
perhaps on a curl of her hair that did not exactly meet
Auguste's demanding standard of perfection.

One day toward the end of June happy shouts and
cheers of the workmen could be heard for blocks around.
At last, Auguste could find nothing to criticize. "She is

perfect," he said. "Let's hail a carriage and take her to
the Fair."

What a sight that was! Her carriage was a wagon
pulled by twelve horses. Thousands of men, women, and
children lined the boulevards to gaze at the gleaming head
riding down the street. Children were heard to ask:
"Where are her hands and her feet and her body?" When
they were told: "Her right arm is miles across the Atlantic
Ocean in America," they were sure it was a fairy tale.

Two life-sized models of the entire statue stood on

Liberty's head at the Paris Fair

each side of the head, which was installed on a pedestal in a small park amid the gilded and enameled buildings at the Fair. Among the dignitaries who were present at the little ceremony, when the head was officially in place for public view, Auguste was pleased to greet his former commanding officer, Gambetta, who was now a leader in French government affairs. During the days that followed, a steady stream of tourists from all over the world climbed the forty-three steps to get a closer look at Liberty's crown.

Little did these spectators realize what a financial struggle it had been for Auguste to complete this great head. There had barely been enough money to pay the men for the last week of work. Now the great shed, that had resounded with hammering and sawing and singing and shouting, was full of gloom and white dust. The money was all gone.

The winter months dragged on and Auguste half-heartedly worked on other projects. The Franco-American Committee held numerous meetings at which Auguste cheered and encouraged the others and urged them not to give up the project. Only Jeanne-Emilie knew how sad and worried he really was. "I will not give up now," he would say over and over. "I cannot desert my daughter Liberty." "Wait for spring," said Jeanne-Emilie. "Good things always happen in the spring."

Something good did happen in the spring. The Committee thought of a wonderful fund-raising plan. They got permission from the French government to sell chances in a lottery. Lotteries were permitted in France for charitable and artistic causes. Senator Bozerian was appointed chairman of the Franco-American Lottery Commission and, in a very short time, he had collected 528 magnificent prizes. Many artists contributed signed paintings to help Miss Liberty. Among the paintings was one by Auguste's good friend Jean Gérôme.

Bartholdi thought of another fund-raising scheme that turned out to be highly successful. He had two hundred copies of his clay "studio model" of the statue cast in bronze. Each of the models was numbered and carried the sculptor's signature. Each one sold as a collectors' item in France and in America for several hundred dollars.

These two projects brought in enough funds to assure the completion of the statue. During the entire campaign money had been contributed by 181 towns and 100,000 individual subscribers. The climax of the fund-raising campaign came on the evening of Wednesday, July 7, 1880 when members of the Franco-American Union and their friends and associates met at a "Notification Dinner." The "Notification" was a beautifully designed message on parchment which notified the United States

> . . . of the assured achievement henceforth of the patriotic work undertaken by the Franco-American Union. The colossal Statue of Liberty, offered by France and consigned to the American Committee, will be completed in 1883. It will be erected by our friends of the United States on a monumental foundation on Bedloe's Island . . . . It will show the two peoples united in this fraternal work as they were one hundred years ago to establish independence.

Among the speakers at the dinner, Auguste was especially pleased to welcome his dear friend Ferdinand de Lesseps. The seventy-five-year-old De Lesseps, who was working on a five-volume history of the Suez Canal, and thinking about another project—the Panama Canal— was only too happy to lend his services on behalf of such a patriotic enterprise.

Never before had there been such activity in the shops at Number 25, Chazelles Street. All day could be heard the happy shouts of men and boys above the constant din of the hammering on copper. Section after section of Liberty's lustrous gown was being fashioned under Bartholdi's watchful eye. In the courtyard a dozen or so men were busy completing a hundred-foot-square brick and concrete block. As the block neared completion, Gustave Eiffel came often to confer with Auguste and the engineer Gaget. It was upon this block that Miss Liberty's wrought-iron skeleton was to be erected. Eiffel was as exacting and as tireless in his work as Auguste. Over a period of five years he had made exhaustive mathematical calculations on the power of resistance of the pieces of iron upon the center of gravity and upon the action of high winds. The most powerful hurricanes ever recorded in Europe and in America were taken as a basis for his calculations.

Before long, neighbors in the workshop area began to wonder at the queer sight they saw from their upstairs windows. Liberty's monster skeleton rose quickly over the housetops like a great naked tower. From the center of the concrete block four huge iron posts pointed to the sky. From these posts spread a network of smaller braces to which Liberty's copper skin was to be anchored. No side show at a circus ever drew more crowds than did the odd sights to be seen at Gaget and Gauthier's. Auguste said that before the statue was completed more than three

Making Liberty's left hand, holding the Tablet of Law

hundred thousand visitors had visited the shop. Beside the skeleton was a mounting pile of various shaped copper pieces backed by sturdy iron straps.

The strangest sights were inside the shop. William Evarts, chairman of the American Pedestal Fund, in Paris as the United States representative to the Paris Monetary Fund, took time from his official duties to pay a call on Miss Liberty. He said it was a "never-to-be-forgotten" experience. In one corner lay a giant finger, taller than a man, with a nail over a foot long. In another corner was an immense foot. "The thing is uncanny," he said to Bartholdi.

Evarts was impressed enough to write a letter to Richard Butler, secretary of the Pedestal Fund, to urge him to call the committee together to renew efforts to raise the money for the pedestal. He said of the magnitude of the statue: "Its size as a structure, although immense, is not out of proportion to the nobleness of the idea."

When the skeleton was completed it had a curious lopsided effect because of the crane-like structure that was to support the arm with the torch. By now the piles of completed copper portions were overflowing the yard. "Soon," said Auguste, "it will be time to start putting some skin on Liberty's bones."

The lines of worry were gone from Auguste's brow. His mother, who came to Paris to celebrate her eighty-first birthday, said she had never seen him in a gayer, happier mood. He was full of excitment over the arrangements he was making with the new American Envoy to France, Levi P. Morton, to participate in the ceremony of driving the first rivet in the first piece of the statue to be mounted to the iron frame. True, all the copper pieces were not ready, but Bartholdi and the workmen were anxious to see the great lady begin to take shape.

The members of the Franco-American Committee decided it would be fitting to hold this ceremony during October, the month of the centenary of the surrender of Cornwallis at Yorktown. The date set for the ceremony was October 24, 1881. Work was all but suspended in the workshop in the excitement of getting ready for the festivities. Liberty's skeleton was gaily decorated with flags. Her head had been returned from the Fair and now sat in the courtyard. "At long last my daughter Liberty," said Bartholdi as he gazed at the head, "you are about to have a body and some feet to stand upon."

The day of the ceremony was beautiful and crisp.

Fifty distinguished gentlemen in frock coats and top hats watched silently while the dignified Levi Morton, a future vice-president of the United States, solemnly took the hammer from Laboulaye and drove the first rivet into the big toe of Liberty's left foot. Morton made a brief talk concerning the plans in America for the reception and erection of the statue. He closed his talk with a wish: "May the statue stand at the entrance of the great harbor of the New World as an illuminated emblem of the friendship between the two republics which will last for all time."

A document, signed by all the guests, which was written on parchment and beautifully ornamented with portraits of Lafayette, Rochambeau, and Washington, was presented to Morton. The document stated:

Today the 24th of October, 1881 . . . Mr. Morton . . . has placed the rivet in the first piece of the Statue of Liberty which will be erected at New York in remembrance of the ancient traditions of friendship which unite the United States to France.

Now the workmen doubled their efforts to complete the sections of the statue. The greatest excitement, of course, was in the courtyard. Every day a section of Liberty's lustrous copper robe was clamped and riveted into place. She was beginning to take shape. Oftentimes Jeanne-Emilie came to admire the beauty of the growing lady. Bartholdi was especially happy when his mother joined Jeanne-Emilie. In his heart he knew he owed much of the success he had attained in realizing his ambition to build a "monument of two nations" to the patient understanding he had received from his mother during the many years.

By midsummer, Liberty's unsightly bony structure was covered almost to the level of her waist. Auguste was so pleased that he decided to invite leading members of the press to a luncheon to formally view the progress that had been made on the statue. What an unusual luncheon it was! Bartholdi was bubbling over with excitement when the twenty guests arrived. He led them directly through the shops and into the courtyard. Without giving them a chance to ask a single question, he motioned for them to follow him through the door into the masonry base. Here, in this great cavern, they followed the sculptor up a wobbly ladder. Above them they could see the blue sky. When it seemed that they had climbed far enough to reach the clouds they suddenly came upon a tremendous platform on which was an attractively decorated table.

"Gentlemen," said Auguste, " I invite you to join me for luncheon on Miss Liberty's knee." It was true. They had climbed up the inside of the statue to the level of Liberty's knee. Dishes, food, and coffee were hauled from below by a rope and a pulley.

With work on the Statue of Liberty going so smoothly, Auguste found time to think of other projects. He completed another patriotic work, a dramatic statue of Rouget de Lisle, composer of the French national anthem, the *Marseillaise,* in time for display at the Salon of 1882. At the same time he displayed a plaster bust of a celebrated Colmarian jurist, d'Ignace Chauffour.

Ten years had sped by since Auguste had visited his native Colmar but he still had the same great love for Alsace. As always it gave him pleasure to make statues of her noted sons. It had been a long time since he had given a new work to Colmar so he decided to present the city with the plaster bust of Chauffour. At home, he spoke more and more of Colmar. His mother, who now spent most of her time in Paris, urged him to go back for a visit. "You can look after some business affairs for me," she said. "And besides," she added, "it will do you good to get away from your daughter Liberty for a while."

So Auguste went. He visited old friends and relatives. He saw his Chauffour on display in the municipal library and was delighted when the city officials asked to have the bust cast in bronze. He went alone to the summer house in the garden and sat for a long time by the banks of the River Lauch and dreamed of his boyhood. Alsace had changed hands, but the war had not changed Auguste's Alsacien heart. No matter where he lived, he would always love Colmar.

Auguste was amazed at Liberty's growth when he got back to Paris. Her arm, which had been sent back from America, stood beside her head in the courtyard. "Soon, my big daughter," he said, "you will be wearing your arm and your head and then you can go to America. I wonder what the Americans are doing about a pedestal for you." Several months before, Auguste had sent plans and detailed drawings of the statue and some sketches of a pedestal to Richard Hunt, who was to design the pedestal. "Seems only yesterday," said Auguste, "instead of twelve years ago when we were all gathered at the La Farges and Richard Hunt thought I was joking when I asked him to design a pedestal for the biggest statue in the world."

Hunt hadn't answered his letter and Auguste couldn't

help wondering if all was going well with the pedestal. Wouldn't do any harm, he decided, to let the Americans know it was time for them to make some haste with the pedestal. In December 1882 he wrote to William Evarts: "The statue commences to reach above the houses, and next spring one will see it overlook the entire city as the large monuments of Paris now do."

"The statue commences to reach above the houses"

9

"GOOD-BYE, MY DAUGHTER LIBERTY"

THE year 1883 was filled with sadness for Auguste. On New Year's Eve his friend and former commanding officer, Gambetta, died after being accidentally shot. Gambetta was only forty-three years old. Henri Martin stood by the open grave and spoke of the sadness of the French nation on losing so great a patriot. In a few months Henri Martin, too, was gone.

The dreary spring wore on. Work on the statue had been deliberately brought to a standstill because the news from America about the pedestal was so disheartening. They didn't have enough money to pay for the foundation, let alone the pedestal. This, despite the fact that the American committee was using every method they could think of to arouse more public interest in the statue. They hired canvassers and a professional speaker to tour the West and talk in Liberty's behalf. They appointed sub-committees of leading citizens in cities outside New York. Even so, New Yorkers were doing most of the contributing.

The architect Hunt now had his pedestal plans ready. The Committee appointed General Charles P. Stone, an army engineer, as engineer-in-chief. General Stone, too, was a friend of Bartholdi. They had met years before in

Egypt. Quarries had been asked to submit samples of granite, and contractors had been asked to submit bids. In the early spring the Committee went through the formalities of breaking ground for the foundation.

Such was the state of affairs when, on May 25th, Liberty's godfather, Edouard de Laboulaye died. United States citizens at home and abroad were saddened by the loss of this devoted champion of America. Out of his love for America he had kindled the flame that led to Bartholdi's patriotic desire to build a Statue of Liberty. Thousands of French from all walks of life came to the funeral to pay their respects to a beloved kinsman.

Seventy-eight-year-old Ferdinand de Lesseps replaced Laboulaye as chairman of the Franco-American Union. De Lesseps, builder of the Suez Canal, member of the Legion of Honor, and president of the French Geographical Society, was full of enthusiasm for the Statue of Liberty. "I am so proud," said Bartholdi, "to have my illustrious friend De Lesseps as an associate in the greatest project of my life."

Butler, secretary of the Pedestal Fund Committee, wrote to De Lesseps expressing the pleasure of the Americans on his appointment as head of the Franco-American Union. He assured De Lesseps and Bartholdi of the early completion of the pedestal. Already, though, Stone was having engineering difficulties. When he began the job of excavation, preparatory to laying the foundation in the middle of the old Star Fort, he dug into heavy masses of stone masonry and concrete. This was not only taking additional time, but it was adding greatly to the cost.

Bartholdi sympathized with the American Committee. He had not forgotten the struggle that it had been to raise funds in France. "I have no fear, however, of your success in America," wrote Bartholdi to Butler. He suggested that some of the fund-raising events that had been successful in France might be tried in America.

Eventually the Committee decided to hold a Pedestal Fund Art Loan Exhibition. They asked prominent artists and writers to donate examples of their work to be auctioned off for the benefit of the pedestal fund. Among those who were invited to contribute was a frail young poetess by the name of Emma Lazarus. Emma, of course, had seen many paintings and drawings of the proposed statue but she had not given any serious thought to the project. So she declined the request, saying, "I am unable to write to order." After she had mailed her refusal, she could not stop thinking about "Liberty Enlightening the World."

A day or so later the Committee was surprised and pleased to receive a poem from Miss Lazarus to include in their portfolio. She had called her poem "The New Colossus." Many years later a bronze tablet bearing the lines of Emma Lazarus's poem was placed in the pedestal of the statue:

> *Not like the brazen giant of Greek fame,*
> *With conquering limbs astride from land to land;*
> *Here at our sea-washed, sunset gates shall stand*
> *A mighty woman with a torch, whose flame*
> *Is the imprisoned lightning, and her name*
> *Mother of Exiles. From her beacon-hand*
> *Glows world-wide welcome; her mild eyes command*
> *The air-bridged harbor that twin cities frame.*
> *"Keep, ancient lands, your storied pomp!" cries she*
> *With silent lips. "Give me your tired, your poor,*

Your huddled masses yearning to breathe free,
The wretched refuse of your teeming shore.
Send these, the homeless, tempest-tost to me,
I lift my lamp beside the golden door!"

When Auguste heard that the month-long exhibition
had brought in a total of $12,000 he was so encouraged
he decided it was time to complete the statue. So great
was the rejoicing of the workmen when the last section
of the flame was riveted into place that no one noticed
Auguste who stood quietly off to one side. It was the
sculptor Simon who saw him. "Are you not happy with
your daughter Liberty?" Simon asked. "It is not Liberty
I'm thinking of," said Bartholdi. "It is of Laboulaye. This
great statue was born of his love for America. I cannot
help but wish he were by my side to share this proud
moment."

To celebrate the statue's completion, a prominent
American businessman in Paris gave a banquet in honor
of Bartholdi. The lavish dinner was attended by French
notables, members of the press, and American diplomats
and businessmen. "Paris should have a statue of 'Liberty
Enlightening the World,' too," said one American. Everyone agreed. Bartholdi promptly offered, without charge,
his thirty-five-foot original plaster working model, should
they want to have a statue cast in bronze. After that there
was much applause and more speeches, and no more was
said about "a little statue for Paris."

A round of dinners and parties honoring Bartholdi
and other members of the Franco-American Union followed. One of the most important was given by Levi
Morton. It was at this dinner that a problem that had

been worrying Auguste for some time was settled: How was he going to get his big statue to America? Numbered among the guests was the Premier of France, Jules Ferry, and Vice-Admiral Peyron of the French Navy. That evening the Admiral announced that the government would convey the great statue to America on a French naval vessel.

Now that the problem of Liberty's transportation was solved, Bartholdi felt free to devote his full attention to planning the ceremony of officially presenting the statue to the American government. The ceremony was to take place on the Fourth of July, 1884. Bartholdi put on his old work clothes and joined the men at Gaget and Gauthier's as they carried pile after pile of boards and chunks of plaster from the shop. When the vast sheds were swept and cleaned, they started on the courtyard.

Under Bartholdi's supervision a huge platform was constructed in front of the statue for the ceremonies. On the morning of the presentation the entire courtyard was decorated in red, white, and blue, and the flags of both nations were prominently displayed. The guests were assembled by eleven o'clock. De Lesseps gave the opening address. He praised all the workers who had helped Bartholdi and then he asked Simon, the sculptor who had worked on Liberty for almost ten years, to come forward. Old Simon, a bit taken aback, looked at Auguste. Auguste's dark eyes were twinkling. "Hurry, Simon," he said. The Minister of Public Instruction was standing beside De Lesseps to greet the bewildered Simon. How proud and happy Auguste was as he watched the Minister bestow the Cross of the Legion of Honor upon his faithful assistant for his work in this patriotic undertaking.

Formal delivery of the Statue to the American government, July 4, 1884

When the cheering died down and the old man, now all crinkled with smiles, got back to his place, De Lesseps turned to Levi Morton and said: "We now transfer to you, Mr. Minister, this great statue and trust that it may forever stand as the pledge of friendship between France and the great republic of the United States." It was a proud moment for Morton, who three years ago had driven the first rivet into the statue. He closed his brief talk with a prayer: "God grant that it may stand until the end of time, as an emblem of imperishable sympathy and affection between the republics of France and the United States."

Now it was time for Auguste to "show off" his dream girl. With all the guests following, he led the way to a big door in the sole of the statue's sandal. Inside the statue the visitors began the long climb up a double spiral staircase to Liberty's crown. The two stairways, one for going up and one for coming down, wound around a central iron column. It was dark inside, wrote Morton in his official report, "with nothing to guide our steps but the thousand and one little eyelets of sunlight that came through the rivet holes." Small wonder that soon a guest asked: "How many steps to the top?" "Only 168 altogether," said Auguste who had made the climb so many times he was unaware others might find it difficult.

"How many stories high is that?" asked another. "About twelve," was the prompt reply. "How far are we now?" panted one of the more rotund gentlemen. "We're already halfway," cheered Auguste. With that, there were loud groans and all but a hardy few crossed over to the companion staircase and turned back.

Those who ventured to the top gazed spellbound from

the crown over the City of Paris. From the great height, Paris was a miniature city of doll houses. But they could easily read the giant Roman letters on the tablet of law in Liberty's left hand—July IV, MDCCLXXVI. Morton was among the hardy ones who followed Bartholdi up the stairway to the elbow of the torch-bearing arm and then up a second flight to the topmost point of the statue.

The Statue of Liberty now officially belonged to America. But America was not ready to welcome her, because they had no pedestal for her to stand on. Stone had just finished the foundation. He had had to make a pit twenty feet deep before he had reached solid ground. Then the great cavity was filled with a mixture of cement, broken stones, and water. Layer after layer of the mixture was beaten down until the whole pit became a solid mass of concrete. The foundation mass was then built up another thirty feet above the ground. This work had cost almost $94,000.

The American Committee would have to raise at least another hundred thousand dollars before Liberty's pedestal could be completed. With barely enough funds in the treasury to get started, the cornerstone for the pedestal was laid on August 5th—a month after the statue had been presented to Morton. That afternoon the clouds hung low over Bedloe's Island and a drenching rain fell, but seven hundred men and a few women came to witness the event. The bedraggled visitors assembled on the top of the man-made foundation stone, where, on the northeast corner, the cornerstone—a fine, large granite block, weighing six tons—hung ready to swing into position.

A sealed copper box containing copies of the Con-

Laying the cornerstone for the pedestal

stitution of the United States and the Declaration of Independence, a history of the statue, daily papers, coins, medals, and other objects of historical interest was placed in a hole in the concrete foundation and the stone was laid over it.

Meanwhile Miss Liberty stayed in Paris and daily welcomed a stream of visitors. On a chill winter day she greeted one of her most ardent admirers and most distinguished guests. He was a tired old gentleman in a frock coat. His white head was bared to the cold. His name— Victor Hugo. Two years before, on his eightieth birthday, 600,000 admirers had taken all day to pass by his house to pay their respects and to leave a mountain of flowers at his door. How proud Bartholdi was to welcome this great writer who came with his daughter Alice and his sprightly granddaughter Jeanne. Madame Bartholdi and Jeanne-Emilie were also on hand to greet Victor Hugo.

Hugo laboriously started to climb the steps inside the statue. He would have gone to the top but his daughter, fearing for his health, stopped him. When he came down he stood for a long time gazing at the statue. Then in a quiet, quavering voice he said: "Yes, this beautiful work holds what I have always loved—called peace. Between America and France . . . this token of peace will live forever; it is well this work is done."

Bartholdi handed the great man a little blue velvet box. "Here," he said, "is a small token of our appreciation for the encouragement you have given 'Liberty Enlightening the World.' " Hugo's deep-sunken eyes glistened when he opened the box and saw a fragment of Liberty's copper engraved with the words:

FRAGMENT
OF THE COLOSSAL STATUE OF LIBERTY
PRESENTED
TO THE ILLUSTRIOUS APOSTLE
OF PEACE, OF LIBERTY, OF PROGRESS
VICTOR HUGO
THE DAY HE HONORED THE WORK OF THE
FRANCO-AMERICAN UNION
WITH HIS VISIT
NOVEMBER 29, 1884

On the following May 13th, Victor Hugo wrote an inscription for a booklet about the statue that Auguste was preparing: "To the sculptor form is everything and is nothing. It is nothing without the spirit—with the idea it is everything." Bartholdi treasured these words. They were perhaps the last Victor Hugo ever wrote because he died eight days after he penned them.

Months had passed since Liberty had been officially presented to Morton. Her lustrous copper robes were dulling. And, always, the first question visitors asked was: "When is she going to the United States?" Frequently Bartholdi heard them say: "They say the Americans don't want her." So Bartholdi decided—pedestal or no pedestal—it was time to ship the statue. It would take several months to take it down and crate it. "By that time," said Auguste, "surely the Americans will have a place for her to stand."

Visitors were no longer allowed to climb the winding stairway to Liberty's crown. Wagonloads of boards and strips of iron piled up in the courtyard. There was a new air of excitement about the shop. Miss Liberty was getting ready to go to her home in Amercia! All day workmen swarmed about the scaffolding filing the rivets to loosen the various pieces of the statue. As the sections were loosened, they were lowered to the ground with the greatest of care so as not to bend or mar them in any way.

On the ground another crew of workmen were busy measuring, sawing, and hammering the hundreds of odd-sized crates needed to pack Liberty's copper skin and her iron bones. Bartholdi checked each piece and made sure that every tiny defect was corrected before the piece was crated. In order to aid in putting the statue up in America, each piece was marked with a particular number or figure. Each two "meeting" pieces were designated by the same sign marked upon their adjoining edges.

It was a slow, tedious job. A sort of quietness came over the workers: "You know," said one, "I'm going to miss the old girl. I didn't realize 'til now how much I really thought of her."

"I have some news to cheer you," said Bartholdi. "France is to have a Statue of Liberty, too."

"You mean we are going to start all over and spend another ten years building another one?" asked the men in astonishment.

"Oh no!" answered Bartholdi. He went on to explain: "A small group of Americans who live in Paris are now taking up a subscription to have the thirty-five-foot studio model cast in bronze to give to France. It will be erected on a pedestal in Paris. I am very honored to have my original model preserved in this manner."

On a warm spring day in early May crowds gathered around the workshops of Gaget and Gauthier to bid good-bye to Miss Liberty. She was about to begin the first stage of her journey. Several wagons made innumerable trips from the shop to the railway station before her 214 crates were finally loaded onto a special train of seventy cars. The train was to take her to the city of Rouen where she would be loaded on the French navy transport, the *Isere*.

The Americans in Paris were anxious to present the "little" statue before the big Liberty sailed. The date set for the ceremony was May 14, 1885. But when that day came, the bronze model was not quite complete. They decided to go ahead with the affair anyway and substitute the plaster model. The plaster model was set on a stone pedestal in a square called Place Etats-Unis (United States). Levi Morton, who had played such a prominent part in Liberty's life, made the formal presentation of the little Liberty to France in the presence of a large gathering of French and American citizens. Several years later the bronze model was placed at the end of a little island in the River Seine in Paris known as the

The "little" Statue of Liberty in Paris

Island of the Swans. A bridge crosses the river there and the statue stands halfway across the bridge.

Even though Gaget and Gauthier both went to Rouen to oversee the loading of the statue, Auguste wanted to be there too. The *Isere* came up the Seine from Cherbourg to Rouen to pick up her precious cargo. She was a sturdy little ship painted white from stem to stern and had been in the service of her country for twenty years.

It took seventeen days to load Liberty. Bartholdi carefully examined each crate before the giant crane gently lifted it from the ground. The packages weighed from 150 pounds to three tons each.

On May 22, 1885, at nine in the morning, the *Isere* lifted anchor. Jeanne-Emilie had come to Rouen to be with Auguste on that day. Also Richard Butler from America was there. Half an hour before the *Isere* sailed, in a pouring rain, a delegation from the city of Rouen, led by the Mayor and a band, came aboard to pay their respects to Auguste and to bid the captain of the ship, Commander Lespinasse de Saune, Godspeed.

Auguste and Jeanne-Emilie stayed aboard until noon when the *Isere* reached the town of Caudelbec-en-Caux on the Seine. They stood on shore and waved until her sails disappeared from sight.

"Good-bye, my daughter Liberty," said Auguste. "At last you are going home."

10

PULITZER, THE *WORLD*, AND LIBERTY

LIBERTY'S voyage began in a storm. For ten days the *Isere* was buffeted by terrific gales. Her sails were reefed to keep them from being torn to shreds. At times, the sixty-five men aboard feared for the safety of the ship. Only Miss Liberty was unconcerned. Bartholdi had made sure that she was so snugly and securely packed that no amount of rolling and tossing would cause her harm.

Ten days passed before the storm subsided. "After that," reported Captain de Saune, "we had light, southerly winds and the sea was smooth. We were able to use both steam and sails." The *Isere* reached America the night of June 17th. She had been under way since May 22nd. However, the date she arrived was a most significant one. It was the hundredth anniversary of the battle of Bunker Hill.

On the morning of the 18th, General Charles P. Stone, engineer-in-chief for the pedestal, along with several French dignitaries, boarded a tug and went out to the *Isere* which had dropped anchor off Sandy Hook. They were cordially greeted by the small, wiry Captain de Saune. He was a pleasant-faced man with reddish-blond hair and whiskers. The Captain and his crew, all smartly uniformed and full of energy, gave no indication of the tiresome trip behind them. The Captain took his guests to his cabin and stood beside a beautiful painting of the Statue of Liberty to conduct the little ceremony of formally transferring his precious cargo to America. "I have the honor," he said to General Stone, "to present to you this parchment, which is a transfer of the statue of 'Liberty Enlightening the World' from my keeping to that of yours."

In accepting the important paper Stone solemnly declared: "I can scarcely express the deep sense of responsibility with which the possession of this document inspires me."

This was perhaps the only quiet moment of the *Isere's* reception. There followed one of the grandest naval pageants the harbor had ever witnessed. Ninety vessels, streamered and flagged, accompanied the *Isere* from

Welcoming the *Isere*

Sandy Hook to Bedloe's Island. Bands played, choral
societies sang, and salutes boomed from the ships and the
harbor forts.

Newspaper reporters poured over the *Isere's* decks,
anxious to see for themselves how the biggest statue in the
world could possibly be packed on one small ship. Captain
de Saune took them below deck. Next day, one of the reporters wrote of the strange sights he had seen when he
peeked between the slats of Liberty's crates:

> When we entered the midship hatchway, an involuntary
> exclamation of surprise escaped us as the huge crown was
> seen, boxed up and extending in a great semi-circle sixty
> feet from end to end. . . . In a case nearby were the
> nose, eyes, and mouth of the statue; in another the eye-
> brows and forehead. . . . The left ear, some pieces of
> the hair, and the crown of the scalp were in a case ten
> by twenty feet while another, eight feet long, held one of
> her curls.

After the naval welcome the ship's crew was paraded
through the decorated streets of New York City to a gala
reception at the City Hall.

The delicate task of unloading the statue began immediately. By means of an immense crane the cases were
gently hoisted through the hatches of the *Isere* and de-
posited on a lighter. There were bundles of iron rods
painted bright vermillion, pieces of internal supporting
columns, and crates of every conceivable size. The lighter,
when loaded, came alongside the dock, and the crane then
lifted the packages to a little car on a tramroad. The car
was pushed along the rails by four men to the crudely

Top: Transferring the statue from the *Isere* to lighters for unloading at Bedloe's Island. *Bottom:* The pedestal at the time of Liberty's arrival in America

constructed sheds that had been built to temporarily house Miss Liberty.

The *Isere* set out for her return voyage on July 3rd. Her officers and crew carried back to France a glowing account of the fine reception they had received in America.

Miss Liberty had indeed been welcomed with warmth and enthusiasm by a hundred thousand cheering Americans. But the grim fact remained: she still had no place to stand. Only a few feet of her eighty-nine-foot pedestal had been constructed. Six months earlier, work on the pedestal had been completely suspended because of lack of funds. It had been resumed only a week before Liberty's arrival.

In the winter of 1884 the Committee had discontinued all work on the pedestal. Then at the urgent appeal of Evarts, chairman of the Fund, various members of the Committee personally pledged a sufficient sum to resume the work at the stone quarries until spring. By that time, they hoped that Congress would make an appropriation for the pedestal.

Spring brought only disappointment. After much wrangling and disagreement Congress failed to make the appropriation. In March the Committee met and heard the gloomy report of the treasurer: "Collected to date, $182,491.40; spent to date, $179,624.51; on hand, $2,-866.89." They did not know which way to turn. They had exhausted every means they could think of to get the needed money. On Friday March 13, 1885, the sad state of affairs was reported by the press under the headline: "Committee Acknowledges Its Inability to Proceed with the Work." Now, only a miracle could save America from the disgrace of having to reject France's gift of "Liberty Enlightening the World."

The miracle did happen. It was brought about by a six-foot frail dynamo named Joseph Pulitzer. Liberty-loving Pulitzer, owner and editor of the New York *World,*

had frequently referred to his paper as "the people's paper." He decided to make a personal appeal to his readers in Liberty's behalf. He opened his campaign for funds on March 16, 1885 with an editorial:

> . . . Nearly ten years ago the French people set about making the Bartholdi statue. It was to be a gift emblematical of our attainment of the first century of independence. It was also the seal of a more serviceable gift they

made to us in 1776, when, but for their timely aid, the
ragged sufferers of Valley Forge would have been dis-
banded and the colonies would have continued a part
of the British dominion. Can we fail to respond to the
spirit that actuated this generous testimonial? . . . The
World is the people's paper, and it now appeals to the
people to come forward and raise the money. . . . Take
this appeal to yourself personally. . . . Give something,
however little. . . .

Pulitzer's "people" did give. Within a week they had
given $2,172.52. Every day the *World* listed the name of
every subscriber, no matter how small the amount. No
editorial appeal for funds was half as potent as these
listings. They were enough to warm a Scrooge's heart:

"Inclosed please find five cents as a poor office boy's
mite to the pedestal fund."

"I am a wee bit of a girl, yet I am ever so glad I was
born in time to contribute my mite to the pedestal fund.
When I am old enough I will ask my papa and mama
to take me to see the statue, and I will always be proud
that I began my career by sending you $1.00 to aid in so
good a cause."

"This fifty cents was my pocket-piece."

"A lonely and very aged woman with limited means
wishes to add her mite."

"We send you $1.00, the money we have saved to
go to the circus with."

Nor was the appeal limited to New York City. Pulitzer
enlisted the aid of the press to appeal to men, women,
and children in cities throughout the United States. Clubs
and other organizations were inspired to give musical,
theatrical, and athletic benefits, the proceeds all go-

ing to the Pedestal Fund. The *World* itself donated $1,000.

On May 11, 1885, only a few days before the sailing of the *Isere,* the Pedestal Fund Committee, encouraged by the results of the *World's* campaign, announced resumption of the work on Bedloe's Island.

The day the statue reached America's shores, the *World* announced it had collected $72,708.95 of the needed $100,000 from 81,116 subscribers. Much of the money had come from school children in individual contributions of less than one dollar.

On August 11, 147 days after Pulitzer had begun his crusade for Liberty, the *World's* front-page headline proclaimed: "One Hundred Thousand Dollars!" At the end of the day, the grand total that had been collected from 120,000 patriotic Americans stood at $102,006.39.

Bartholdi was jubilant when the news of Pulitzer's success reached Paris. He wrote to Butler: "I have a great desire to see how the work is getting on and to settle with General Stone about the erection of the statue. In one hour of conversation we will be able to do more than in six months' correspondence." Jeanne-Emilie was just as anxious as Auguste to go to America.

They sailed on the *SS Amérique* on October 24th and arrived in New York on the morning of November 5th. Bartholdi's first words to the press when he arrived were: "To the *World* not only my thanks but the hearty commendation of the French Republic are due for the noble aid it has rendered in the project of erecting a symbol of liberty in this harbor."

A few days later the Bartholdis went out to Bedloe's Island to see the work on the pedestal. Auguste was well aware of the engineering problems encountered by General Stone in erecting a pedestal for a statue of such great size. In his usual slow, methodical way Auguste carefully examined the work. He expressed pleasure at the beauty of the gray granite that was being used for the exterior face of the pedestal. The granite blocks, which averaged three feet in thickness, came from Leete's Island, Connecticut. The inner wall of the pedestal was of concrete, in layers six inches thick. "Liberty's future is safe in your hands," Auguste said to Stone. "When this pedestal is finished it will be as solid as the Rock of Gibraltar."

"I should never have had doubts about the pedestal," Auguste later confided to Jeanne-Emilie.

"You have devoted most of your life to this statue," she replied. "It is only natural that you cannot leave a single detail in another's hands, no matter how competent those hands may be."

How right Jeanne-Emilie was! Auguste did not rest until he had gone over every step of the job of anchoring and assembling the statue. He had no fault to find with General Stone's carefully planned system of support and anchorage of the statue by means of heavy steel girders which were to be imbedded into the pedestal.

"When finished," said Stone, "this pedestal will be one of the heaviest pieces of masonry ever constructed. The material in the pedestal and the foundation mass will weigh over 28,000 tons. The statue, the pedestal, and the foundation are being so anchored together and to the island that the only way the statue could fall, would be if the island itself would upturn." Auguste smilingly agreed that the possibility of the island's being uprooted was highly unlikely.

The Bartholdis' three-week stay in America was by no means devoted entirely to conferences and work. They were entertained at a round of parties and dinners by individuals as well as by civic clubs. Bartholdi left for Paris with his mind completely at rest so far as his daughter Liberty was concerned. No date for her completion was set but "whenever she is ready," Auguste said, "I will drop all other work and return to America for the unveiling ceremonies."

Almost every day during the Bartholdis' visit the sun had smiled down on Bedloe's Island. The crisp cold air was just right for the vigorous work on the pedestal. But as winter progressed, Miss Liberty was often cold and alone as icy, biting winds kept the workmen away.

It was April before the last stone of the pedestal was put into place. Mortar for the last block was sprinkled with pennies, nickels, and dimes as a symbol of the generosity of the Americans who had made the structure possible. The building of the foundation and the pedestal had required two years of continuous work.

Auguste had closely followed the work on the pedestal through correspondence with Butler. When word reached him that the pedestal was nearing completion, he sent one of his most skilled workmen to America to help with the stupendous task of assembling and erecting the statue.

The first step in mounting the statue to the pedestal was the erection of the huge iron skeleton. Each individual iron bone in Liberty's skeleton had to be fitted in exactly the right place. This would have been a comparatively simple task except that some of her bones had been mislabeled. Sometimes it was necessary to raise, try, and lower as many as twenty pieces before the right one was found. This was no light task since each piece had to be hoisted two hundred feet to the top of the pedestal. Three months passed before Liberty's skeleton was completed.

Americans were as fascinated as the Parisians had been by the weird sight of Liberty's giant skeleton. An endless stream of men, women, and children flocked to the island to watch the building of the biggest statue in the world. On July 12th the first two of Liberty's 300 pieces of copper skin were ceremoniously riveted into place. The first rivet was christened Bartholdi and his name was inscribed in the copper plate beside the rivet. Pulitzer was honored in the same fashion on the second plate.

Many of the copper pieces had been labeled wrong and some of the labels had disappeared entirely. Also, a certain amount of distortion had taken place during the time Liberty had been stored, so sometimes the pieces had to be refitted before they could be riveted into place. Seventy-five men were engaged in the slow, painstaking work. The mounting required 600,000 rivets and each one had to be driven carefully and accurately so that the statue would not be disfigured in any way.

"Are they Lilliputians?" children asked as they gazed up and up at the workmen suspended on pulleys over the giant statue. Scaffolding was not put up around the statue for the men to stand on as had been done when the statue was made in Paris.

In addition to driving the rivets, it was necessary for the workmen to place a piece of asbestos insulation in every place where copper and iron touched. Otherwise the copper Liberty, at the mercy of the moist sea air, might corrode and disintegrate. "Without such insulation, it was even possible," warned Eiffel, the designer of the skeleton, "that Liberty could turn into a giant electric battery and shock her visitors."

Children, and grownups, too, often asked the workmen: "What will happen to Miss Liberty if she gets struck by lightning?"

"Nothing will happen to her," was the reply. "Copper rods soldered to the inside of the statue pass through the

The Statue of Liberty nearing completion

pedestal and down into the wet ground below. If lightning did strike her, it could do no harm."

As the statue approached completion, the Pedestal Fund Committee began to make arrangements for the dedication ceremonies. Congress appropriated $56,500 ". . . for construction of platform, repairs of wharf, clearing grounds of unsightly structures, . . . and for incidental expenses of the ceremony of inauguration."

The American Electric Manufacturing Company generously presented the committee with an electric plant to light Liberty's torch.

Auguste Bartholdi's dream of a "monument of two nations" was about to come true. President Grover Cleveland issued invitations to French dignitaries to attend the "Inaugural Ceremonies of Liberty Enlightening the World" to be held on October 28, 1886.

11

LIBERTY AT HOME

THE last piece of Liberty's copper was riveted into the sole of her right sandal on Saturday, October 23, 1886. Late in the evening of the next day, the French delegates to the inaugural ceremonies arrived in New York aboard the *Bretagne*. A week before the delegation sailed from France Auguste's mother became very ill and he rushed to Colmar to be by her side. He wrote to Butler: "I am in a very painful situation. My mother is sick. I do not know whether I shall be able to come over or not. I would be very sorry, dear friend, to lose this opportunity to enjoy with you the fulfilling of all our hopes and the successful ending of all our troubles. I confess I feel sad about it."

But Madame Bartholdi refused to allow Auguste to give up the trip. "You must go," she insisted. "You belong with your daughter Liberty on the most important day in her life." She wouldn't allow Jeanne-Emilie to stay with her either. "Auguste needs you by his side," she said.

So Auguste and Jeanne-Emilie did as she bade them. Now as the ship sailed into harbor they stood on deck and waited, hand-in-hand, to catch the first glimpse of Liberty. But it was foggy and all they could see was an indistinct outline of the statue.

A distinguished welcoming party met the delegates

and took them immediately aboard a yacht bound for Bedloe's Island. Auguste was plainly disappointed at not being able to see the statue. "I assure you," said Butler, "that your statue is exactly as you planned it to be." Somewhat reassured, Auguste reluctantly went below for refreshments.

Jeanne-Emilie stayed on deck with Tototte, Ferdinand de Lesseps' thirteen-year-old daughter. In a few moments the fog began to lift and the statue came into view. All of a sudden Jeanne-Emilie started shouting. "Look, look, Tototte. Look at that arm. There is something wrong. There is a big black lump that should not be. Do you see it?"

Jeanne-Emilie was most surprised when Tototte started laughing. "Look closely and you'll see why I'm laughing," she said. "That lump you see is a man. He is probably giving the arm and the torch a final check."

All Auguste's fears and anxieties disappeared as he examined the statue on Bedloe's Island. "When I first came to America, I dreamed of this," said Bartholdi. "I said to myself, 'what a great thing it would be for this statue to be placed in the midst of such a scene of life and liberty'. My dream has been realized. I can only say that I am enchanted. This thing will live to eternity, when we shall have passed away, and everything living with us has moldered away."

Bartholdi turned and followed Miss Liberty's gaze out to sea toward France. A solemn-faced little boy, no doubt one of the workmen's children, came over to Auguste. "I love her too," he said. "Here is a chip of the stone from her pedestal. Would you like to have it?"

Bartholdi eagerly accepted the gift. He unbuttoned his

great coat and put the bit of stone in an inside pocket as if for safekeeping. Then he stooped down and amazed the little boy by kissing him first on one cheek and then the other.

Auguste would happily have spent several hours with Miss Liberty. The faint glow from the few oil lamps cast weird shadows in the cavern of the great statue. Tototte was fascinated and urged her none-too-nimble father to go to the top with her. Auguste, too, wanted to climb to the torch to see for himself the lighting arrangements.

But there was no time. The delegation was scheduled to take a boat trip around Manhattan and afterwards to attend a banquet. The official reception committee had outdone themselves to see that the French delegates were properly entertained.

The list of Americans who had given generously of their time and their money for the benefit of the pedestal was an impressive one. Cyrus Field, William Waldorf Astor, John and William Jay, J. P. Morgan, and many others attended the round of receptions and banquets honoring Bartholdi and the other French delegates.

Wednesday, October 27, 1886, Bartholdi was received by the Mayor at the City Hall and, in the presence of other French delegates and members of the Board of Aldermen, was presented with a document giving him "full freedom" of the city. Thursday was officially designated "Bartholdi Day" and was proclaimed a holiday.

In a cold, drizzling rain, a million Americans stood elbow to elbow alongside the five-mile mud-plastered route to watch the Bartholdi Day parade. "The city was one vast cheer," reported the *World*. Wet and soggy American and French flags waved valiantly from every conceivable spot. There were miles and miles of red, white, and blue bunting. The most spectacular display was the sixty-foot-high evergreen-covered arch which spanned the street in front of the *World* building. On top of the arch were two giant globes with a Statue of Liberty in between.

President Cleveland and members of his Cabinet, Governor Hill of New York and his staff, Bartholdi, De Lesseps, and other dignitaries reviewed the two-and-a-half-hour procession from an especially constructed stand in Madison Square. Soldiers, veterans, bands, students, firemen, members of French military and civic societies— 20,000 in all—passed by to pay their respects to Auguste Bartholdi.

Among these thousands was an old, and very dear, friend of Auguste. Leading a small group of Colmarians at the head of the French column was Chrétien Mugel, former chef at the Hotel of the Two Keys in Colmar. After the Franco-Prussian War, Chrétien and his wife had come to America to live and Chrétien had organized the little band of Alsaciens in New York into a "Colmarian Society." Bartholdi leaned down from the stand to greet his childhood friend. "Remember," he said, "years ago when I received the Cross of the Legion of Honor in Colmar and I could not believe it was true. Today, Chrétien, I feel exactly the same way. I am wondering, is all this true?"

His faithful friend smiled warmly. "Same as then," he said. "It is really true."

A little later three small girls, each holding a basket of flowers, stopped before the stand. "These are for the President," they said as they handed them up to the platform. The President, quite pleased, thanked them. Then one of the little girls, who said her name was May, shook out the folds of a handsome silken banner on an ornamental staff. On one side was the Stars and Stripes and on the other was the French flag. "This is not for the President," she said. "It's for Mister Bartholdi." The inscription embroidered in a corner of the banner said:

TO M. BARTHOLDI
IN MEMORY OF LIBERTY-LOVING FRANCE
NEW YORK, 1886
PRESENTED BY MAY FEST

The procession lasted so long there was no time for lunch before the delegates had to rush to the ship to view the spectacular naval parade of three hundred vessels. After the naval parade, the dignitaries assembled on Bedloe's Island on an immense platform which had been erected for the occasion. All except Auguste. He had a special place of honor high in Liberty's torch. At a signal from a boy three hundred feet below Auguste would pull the cord to release the tri-color veil from Liberty's face.

The exercises began with a prayer. The first speaker was De Lesseps, his silky white hair and mustache looking well groomed despite the weather. Tototte, holding his battered silk hat, stood primly beside him while he spoke on behalf of the Franco-American Union. Then Evarts rose to present the statue to President Cleveland "to the care and keeping of the Government of the United States."

He spoke a few sentences and paused to take a breath. Auguste, of course, could hear nothing of the proceedings. He had eyes only for the "signal" boy. When Evarts paused, the boy thought he was finished with his speech so he gave the signal. This was the moment Auguste had waited so many, many years for. He pulled the cord and pandemonium broke loose. Evarts, startled by the outburst, was sure the enthusiasm was not for his words. But

A GIFT
FROM
THE PEOPLE OF THE REPUBLIC OF FRANCE
TO THE PEOPLE OF THE UNITED STATES.
THIS STATUE
OF
LIBERTY ENLIGHTENING THE WORLD
COMMEMORATES THE ALLIANCE OF THE TWO NATIONS
IN ACHIEVING THE INDEPENDENCE
OF THE
UNITED STATES OF AMERICA.
AND
ATTESTS THEIR ABIDING FRIENDSHIP.
AUGUSTE BARTHOLDI.
SCULPTOR.
INAUGURATED
OCTOBER 28TH 1886.

Dedication plaque on the Statue of Liberty

he was about to go on when, seeing the direction in which the cheering spectators were looking, he realized what had happened. He gave up and sat down.

For fifteen minutes cannons from the men-of-war boomed out their salutes, whistles blew, bells rang, and patriots cheered wildly. In between it all the red-plumed, white helmets of the members of Gilmore's Band bobbed alternately to the tunes of *Yankee Doodle* and the *Marseillaise.*

President Cleveland rose and Gilmore shifted to *Hail to the Chief* midst a fresh outburst of cheers. The President waited a few moments and the crowd quieted. He spoke solemnly: "We will not forget that Liberty has here made her home; nor shall her chosen altar be neglected. Willing votaries will constantly keep alive its fires, and these shall gleam upon the shores of our sister Republic in the East. Reflected thence, and joined with answering rays, a stream of light shall pierce the darkness of ignorance and man's oppression, until liberty enlightens the world."

Bartholdi came down from the heights to take his place on the stand. There were other speeches but they were lost on Bartholdi. His mind and his heart were still in the clouds with his big daughter Liberty.

Once the ceremonies were over, the milling crowds became suddenly mindful of the disagreeable weather. There was a mad rush to get home. At five o'clock the President boarded his special train for Washington. The rain showed no signs of letting up and the ceremony of lighting the torch and the $2,500 fireworks display was postponed until "the first dry evening."

Rain did not dampen the enthusiasm of the several hundred guests who paid honor to Bartholdi and the other members of the French delegation at a gay banquet given by the New York City Chamber of Commerce. Auguste was deeply touched when he was presented with two white silk badges which had been worn by Lafayette when he visited America in 1824.

New York stayed damp and soggy. So Liberty continued to have no light. The Bartholdis joined a large party of friends on a special excursion to Niagara Falls. The day after they left the weather cleared and Liberty had her fireworks christening. Thousands came to witness the display. Auguste, of course, was still in Niagara Falls and the significance of the lighting of the torch was lost in the more spectacular fireworks display.

The spectacular fireworks display in Liberty's honor

The delegates returned to New York in time to rush to a luncheon and then on to an evening banquet. Early the next morning they left for Washington to be received by the President.

Meanwhile, the American committee was having

trouble keeping the statue lighted. The donors of the electric plant had agreed to keep it going for only one week after the ceremonies. It wasn't their fault, they said, that the light hadn't been turned on according to schedule.

The government had made no provision for Liberty's light. It was due to go out on November 5th and Auguste still hadn't seen it. The electric company finally agreed to keep the light burning until January, but the company that supplied the boiler and the motive power wasn't so co-operative. They agreed to keep it going only through November 6th.

The French delegation came back from Washington in time to attend a banquet in honor of the members of the Pedestal Fund Committee.

On the evening of November 6th, Auguste, Jeanne-Emilie, and Richard Butler finally were free to go to the shore to see Liberty's torch cast her rays of light.

For years Bartholdi had made known his desire that Liberty should enlighten the world realistically as well as symbolically. He wanted a great beam of light that could be seen for miles and miles to shine from the uplifted torch. In a day when electric lighting itself was in its infancy (the first electric lighting plant in the United States had been established in New York City only four years before), this was a fantastic wish. Thomas A. Edison, who had generously contributed $250 to the Pedestal Fund, was still making improvements on his incandescent lamp which he had patented in 1880.

It was small wonder then that all Auguste saw was a faint glimmer from Liberty's torch. The newspapers said it looked like a glowworm. Auguste was disappointed, but certainly not discouraged. The next night, as scheduled, Liberty's feeble light was extinguished. "I know," said Bartholdi, "Liberty's torch will burn again and, some day, it will shine in all its glory."

A few mornings later at breakfast, Auguste and Jeanne-Emilie were gayly discussing the many parties and banquets they had yet to attend. Auguste was especially looking forward to the evening when he was to be presented with a silver testimonial. For years he had given unstintingly of his time to Liberty, with no thought of remuneration. In fact, much of his own fortune had gone into the making of the statue. The committee was well aware of all the sacrifices he had made and when the *World's* campaign went over the $100,000 goal, they asked Pulitzer's permission to use $1,000 for a suitable memento for Bartholdi.

Tiffany's had been commissioned to design the gift and for a number of days it had been displayed in their window for all to admire. "Truly," Bartholdi said, "I am looking forward to the testimonial banquet. I must admit the thought of receiving that magnificent token excites me."

A knock on the door interrupted their happy conversation. A boy handed Auguste a cable. It was from friends in Colmar. Auguste read it and then handed it to Jeanne-Emilie. She read: "Your mother dangerously ill. Come home at once."

Gifts, parties, dinners were all forgotten in the Bartholdis' rush to pack. Fortunately, they were able to book passage on a ship sailing the next morning. News of their departure spread quickly and soon their room was filled with sympathetic friends.

When they boarded the ship next morning Auguste's heart was heavy with worry and concern for his mother. However, his sad eyes lighted with pleasure for a few moments when a delegation came aboard to bid him good-bye and to present the souvenir he was to have received at the banquet.

On a globe of silver, France and the main rivers of the world were inlaid in gold and Bartholdi's head was in relief in silver. On top of the globe was Liberty's arm and torch. The base was made of petrified wood from Arizona and it was decorated in silver reliefs of Bartholdi,

The silver testimonial presented to Bartholdi

some sculptor's tools, views of Liberty, and a printing press in honor of the *World*. There were two inscriptions:

ALL HOMAGE AND THANKS
TO THE
GREAT SCULPTOR, BARTHOLDI

A TRIBUTE
FROM THE NEW YORK WORLD
AND
OVER 121,000 AMERICANS
TO
AUGUSTE BARTHOLDI
AND
THE GREAT LIBERTY LOVING PEOPLE OF FRANCE
1886

Bartholdi, who usually was never at a loss for words said: "I find it hard to say the words in English to express my feelings. Hear my thanks, dear friends, with your hearts as well as your ears."

As the ship sailed away to France, Auguste waved to his statue. "Good-bye, my daughter Liberty," he said. "I am glad you are home at last."

Liberty's feeble light was glowing again before Auguste reached France. The United States now owned the statue, but when the light went out no one knew what branch of the government was supposed to maintain it. On November 16th, President Cleveland directed that the statue be "at once placed under the care and superintendence of the Lighthouse Board and that it be from henceforth maintained by said Board as a beacon." A few days later the Lighthouse Board kindled Liberty's little flame again. The cost of keeping it lit was estimated at $8.50 per year.

Bartholdi found his mother somewhat improved, but he spent the winter going back and forth from Paris to Colmar to keep close watch over her. The unsatisfactory lighting of Liberty caused him much worry. Even though the statue now officially belonged to America, he still somehow felt personally responsible because she was not properly lighted.

Everywhere in the Bartholdis' house were reminders of the Statue of Liberty. The first thing Bartholdi saw when he opened his front door was a model of the thumb of Liberty along the length of the wall. Nearby on the floor was an ear, large enough to seat two people. His studio was filled with models of the statue in various sizes and stages of completion. In one large glass case was a miniature Liberty against a background painting of a panorama of New York. When John La Farge came to Paris to receive the Cross of the Legion of Honor for a magnificent glass window he exhibited at the Paris Exhibition of 1889, he said that just being in Bartholdi's studio made one homesick for America.

Auguste had time now to complete a number of works that he had put aside for so many years. He went to Clermont-Ferrand to complete the arrangements for his statue of Vercingetorix—arrangements that had been interrupted years before by the Franco-Prussian War.

He went more and more often to Colmar to see his mother. Each time it became harder for him to leave. Finally, seeing the concern she was causing her son, the old lady agreed to come to Paris to stay. It made Auguste

Auguste Bartholdi in his studio

and Jeanne-Emilie very happy to have her there with them. Under their loving care she seemed to grow stronger. One day Auguste was busy in his studio when he was startled by cries of "Help! Help!" He found his mother crumpled on the hall floor. Somehow she had slipped and broken her leg.

That was in January 1889, and from that time on, Madame Bartholdi was an invalid and remained in her room. On her ninetieth birthday they had a gay celebration in her room. Auguste thought his mother, with her white curls framing her proud face, had never looked more beautiful. Less than a month later, on October 25, 1891, she passed away.

Shortly after the death of his mother, Auguste received another crushing blow. "At least," he said, "I have some satisfaction in that my mother did not have to share the grief that the city of Paris is causing me." The Bartholdis were being forced to move from their home because the city wanted to make a street where the house stood. Auguste had lived and worked in that house for thirty-eight years and he tried every legal means he knew to save it but, in the end, the City had its way. "My old house is now broken down," wrote Bartholdi to Butler, "and the cars will soon run over the place of my studio."

Auguste could find no place to move that satisfied him. He and Jeanne-Emilie took temporary quarters in a small apartment and Auguste began making plans to have a new house built.

All this time he had not for one moment forgotten Liberty or America. He had found time to design a statue of Columbus which an American silver manufacturer was executing in silver for display at the Chicago World's Fair of 1893. At the Salon of 1892 he had exhibited a model of a statue of Washington and Lafayette. Pulitzer had already indicated a desire to present a bronze of this group to Paris and Auguste hoped to place a replica in America. He made plans to exhibit his Washington and Lafayette at the Chicago Fair.

Bartholdi had been in constant correspondence with Butler and with the Lighthouse Board concerning the lighting of the Statue of Liberty. Seven years had sped by since he had seen his daughter Liberty. He wanted to see for himself how America was treating her. "I would like to go to America too," said Jeanne-Emilie. "It will be time enough to build a new house when we come back."

On August 9, 1893 Auguste wrote to Butler: "We shall have very soon the pleasure to shake your dear hand. We sail on the 26th of this month on the *SS Champagne.*"

12

LIBERTY ENLIGHTENING THE WORLD

THE sun had already gone down when the *SS Champagne* reached America on September 2, 1893. All Auguste could see of his colossal statue was a dark, hazy shadow, topped by a faint glimmer of light. "Some day, somehow," said Auguste as he strained his eyes trying to pierce the darkness, "surely a way to light the statue will be found."

Next day, newspaper reporters called at the small French hotel where the Bartholdis chose to stay, "because," said Auguste, "my wife, who speaks only French, is more comfortable here." In answer to a reporter's query: "What is the purpose of your visit?" the sculptor promptly replied: "I came to visit the Statue of Liberty."

After the interview, one of the reporters remarked to another: "Does it not seem strange to you that a man would cross the ocean to see a statue that he had already looked at for ten years."

"Not so strange," replied the other. " I believe he really likes the old girl. I've heard that he thinks of her as a member of his own family."

Before the Bartholdis visited Bedloe's Island, they went to the top floor of one of New York's new "skyscrapers" and viewed the statue. Also they got an excellent view of Liberty from the dome of Pulitzer's new *World* building. It was sunset by the time they reached the island. The statue was flooded with the red beams. "She is indeed a Goddess of Liberty and glory," exclaimed Bartholdi. He eagerly climbed the steps to Liberty's torch. He was highly pleased with the electric lights which replaced the old lanterns inside the statue and pedestal. "Now," he said, "visitors can see clearly the intricate work of Liberty's skeleton." He carefully examined every part of the torch. "I have no fault to find with the condition of the statue," he said.

Due to exposure to the elements Liberty was covered from her torch to her toes with a soft green coat. Bartholdi thought her dark color made it more difficult to illuminate her, and after several consultations with the lighting experts, he wrote in his recommendations: "I think at first the best plan would be to have the statue gilded, but if this is too expensive, perhaps the statue could be painted in such a manner that it would appear metallic."

Now that Auguste's mind was at peace concerning his statue, the Bartholdis decided to visit the World's Fair in Chicago. Bartholdi's silver Columbus was there as well as his Washington and Lafayette.

On their return from Chicago Auguste made one more trip to the statue. The afternoon before they sailed for France he spent a long time at Bedloe's Island. "It was," said Jeanne-Emilie, "as if he could not bear the thought of leaving Liberty."

"Good-bye again, my daughter," said Auguste the next morning as they sailed away. They watched until Liberty was nothing but a tiny speck in the far distance.

Jeanne-Emilie's eyes filled with tears. "We will come back and see her again," she said.

"I don't know," said Auguste sadly.

Although there was an ocean between them, not for one moment did Auguste forget his big daughter. He kept in close touch with the Citizens' Committee which had been formed for the purpose of keeping the statue open to the public and to provide ferry boat service to and from the island. Many of the members of the former Pedestal Fund Committee, including Richard Butler, served with the new group.

Through correspondence with Butler, Auguste was kept informed of the activities of the three agencies that at this time had control of the statue—the Army, which controlled the military reservation on the island and performed guard functions around the statue; the Lighthouse Board which maintained the light; and the Citizens' Committee. "Poor Liberty," said Bartholdi to Jeanne-Emilie after reading a letter from Butler. "I fear her well-being is further complicated by friction among the three agencies that are supposed to take care of her."

Auguste worried about the situation but there was nothing he could do about it. His own personal life was so complicated, he hardly had time to answer Butler's letters. "My days," he wrote to Butler, "are always hurried, disturbed. My mind has been somewhat influenced by the material disorganization of my life." He was having problems with the construction of his new house. Work had been started on the house shortly after the Bartholdis' return from America. By the following summer the house was only partially finished. The studio part barely had a roof over it. But Auguste was impatient to get settled so they moved in anyway. For months they lived in a complete state of confusion. In his anxiety to have the house exactly as he wanted it, Auguste was constantly making changes. Furniture was in complete disarray and many times unexpected guests had to sit on boxes or trunks.

By New Year's Day the dining room, which was the most unusual room in the house, was finished. Auguste and Jeanne-Emilie were able, as had been their custom for many years, to invite friends and relatives to a great feast. Sixty-one-year-old Bartholdi, looking picturesque in his silk Lavaliere cravat tied in a flowing bow under his pointed gray beard, beamed like a child as guests admired the array of fine porcelain that decorated the walls.

While Auguste decorated his house with objects of art from all parts of the world, his heart remained faithful to Alsace. The main dish at his New Year's dinner was always the same—the traditional sauerkraut of Alsace. This simple food, decorated with little tri-color flags of France, was brought to the table with great ceremony. Bartholdi had never given up the hope that one day Alsace would again belong to France. Oftentimes for a gift he painted a watercolor which showed a white marker pointing toward Alsace surrounded by blue forget-me-nots and red poppies.

Affairs of property required Auguste to go quite often to Colmar. He loved to walk the streets and greet and shake hands with his many old friends and with their children and their grandchildren. Such visits usually resulted in his doing another statue for his native city.

Doctors urged him to work less and rest more, but Auguste was not one to stay idle. There were many statues he felt he must do. He could hardly rest at all until Pulitzer's gift of Washington and Lafayette to the city of Paris was unveiled. Several years later a replica of this same group was presented to New York City.

For some time Auguste had suffered great pain with rheumatism. Then he contracted tuberculosis. It became necessary for him to go often to the south of France to rest in the sunshine and to soak his ailing knee in the mineral waters. The moment he began to feel better, he would hurry back to Paris to go to work.

He finally finished Vercingetorix. It had taken the founder eleven months just to cast the giant statue of the ancient Gaul on a horse. Now it was finished. How was Auguste going to get it to Clermont-Ferrand? The statue on its pedestal was too heavy to ship on one of the freighters that steamed up and down the River Seine. It was too big to send by rail. The ailing Auguste stubbornly refused to ship the statue and its pedestal in pieces. "I will drag Vercingetorix and his horse over the roads to Clermont-Ferrand myself, if necessary," said Auguste good-humoredly.

Fortunately Auguste was spared attempting this feat. A manufacturer of the new steam-driven carriages, anxious to publicize his own product, offered to transport the statue in an especially constructed vehicle. What a ride that was! Everywhere, on the open roads, and through the winding, narrow streets of the many villages, cheering crowds followed the truck with its strange cargo of a giant bronze man on a horse. Once, during the six-day drive, an excited onlooker ran in front of the vehicle. The driver swerved the vehicle sharply and the statue began to waver back and forth. The crowd stood spellbound waiting for the rugged horseman to crash to the ground. But it didn't. Somehow the statue was able to regain its balance and the harried driver was able to go on to Clermont-Ferrand.

Another statue that Bartholdi had neglected during the many years he labored on Liberty was one of a balloon to honor the brave aeronauts who had flown people, mail, and homing pigeons over the enemy lines during the siege of Paris in 1870-71. Auguste finished this statue but he did not live to see it unveiled.

He became more and more disabled. Even letter-writing, especially in English, became a task. Auguste, always hungry for news of his daughter Liberty, tried very hard to keep up the correspondence with the Citizens' Committee in America. Once he wrote to Butler: "Excuse my mistakes; if you hear of a typewriter that would print in English, being played in French, let me know! In the meantime read the letters in the heart of your faithful friend."

In 1902 Auguste had word that President Theodore Roosevelt had transferred control of the statue from the Lighthouse Board to the War Department. The sculptor's big daughter had been pretty much neglected by the American government since her unveiling sixteen years ago. Now, with only one government agency responsible for her well-being, Auguste hoped she would fare better.

Some days Auguste would spend hours in his studio looking over all his various models of Liberty. "If I could go to America just once more, I would be happy," said Auguste. Jeanne-Emilie answered: "Rest, and do as the doctor orders, and you will grow strong again, and then we will visit your beautiful Liberty."

But Auguste would not give up working. He quite cheerfully began work on a new project—his own funeral monument. When he finished his own tombstone, he took to his bed and never got up again. He died on October 4, 1904.

His death was deeply mourned in Colmar. Many Colmarians made the trip to Paris to attend the funeral. Jeanne-Emilie received expressions of sympathy from Auguste's many friends throughout the world. Among these was a cablegram from the President of the United States, Theodore Roosevelt: "Permit me to offer, in the name of the American people, my deep sympathy on the occasion of the death of the great sculptor, your husband."

Soon there was a new statue in Colmar. This one was not *by* the sculptor, who for so many years had embellished his native city with works of art, but it was a statue *of* Auguste Bartholdi. The statue, which may be seen today in Colmar, depicts Bartholdi with his right arm resting on a modelling stand. On the stand is a model of the Statue of Liberty. Auguste holds a sculptor's tool in his right hand as if he had just finished his Liberty Enlightening the World.

Many of Auguste Bartholdi's dreams have, with the passing of time, come true. His beloved Colmar was restored to France as a result of the Allied victory in World War I.

The war also stimulated interest in the Statue of Liberty as a symbol of freedom and democracy. Again, as in 1885, it was the New York *World* that took the lead in raising funds for Liberty. This time the funds were to provide adequate lighting for the statue. Late in 1915, the *World,* after consulting artists, engineers, and electrical

Bartholdi with his "Liberty Enlightening the World"

experts submitted detailed plans to the War Department for improving the torch lighting and installing a permanent floodlighting system. The newspaper, under the leadership of Joseph Pulitzer's sons, proposed to raise by popular subscription the necessary $30,000 to install the lighting plant. The War Department agreed to maintain the plant.

On May 24, 1916, the *World* announced the opening of the drive for funds and started the campaign with a donation of $1,000. What a contrast this campaign was to the *World's* Pedestal Fund campaign! This time there was no pleading for money. Americans, sympathetic to the cause of the Allies, gave generously. The Vice-President of the United States, Thomas R. Marshall, expressed the sentiment of the people when he said: "The statue in New York Harbor of Liberty Enlightening the World should always have been lighted up at night."

Money began to pour in from citizens in all parts of the United States. A month after the campaign started a great munitions explosion occurred on Black Tom wharf only a half mile from Miss Liberty. The explosion shook down buildings for miles around—$100,000 damage was done to structures on Bedloe's Island alone. All over the United States, patriotic Americans clamored for news of the fate of "our" Statue of Liberty.

They need not have worried. Auguste Bartholdi once said: "This statue will live forever." People were beginning to realize how well Auguste had done his work. The statue was damaged only slightly. Even the light in her torch, feeble as it was, continued to burn throughout the explosion.

America suddenly was ashamed of that feeble light.

"It should have been illuminated years ago," was the message that accompanied the contributions for a new lighting system. In less than six months, the necessary money had been raised. The sculptor Gutzon Borglum, now famed for his giant figures of Washington, Jefferson, Lincoln, and Theodore Roosevelt, carved on the granite face of Mount Rushmore in the Black Hills of South Dakota, was engaged to supervise the remodeling of the torch. The new lighting also included an elaborate system of floodlighting.

At sunset, on December 2, 1916, President Woodrow Wilson gave a wireless signal which turned on the lights. Thousands of Americans who lined the shores of New York Harbor saw Liberty, in the words of the *World:* "transformed suddenly from a black and shapeless bulk against a rapidly darkening sky into a glorious Goddess bathed in golden light." At the moment Liberty was lighted, an illuminated airplane circled overhead. On the bottom of the plane the word "Liberty" was spelled in glowing letters. Thirty years after her unveiling, Auguste's big daughter Liberty finally "shone in all her glory"!

With America's entrance into World War I the statue took on a personal meaning for millions of boys who sailed away to fight. She was the symbol of the freedom and the democracy for which they were fighting. When they returned, they wept with joy as she came into sight, for she was also the symbol of home.

"Liberty Enlightening the World" was beginning to mean as much to Americans as she had always meant to Bartholdi. Never again would she suffer the neglect of her first thirty years. In 1924 President Calvin Coolidge proclaimed the Statue of Liberty a National Monument.

The Statue of Liberty "bathed in golden light"

More and more men, women, and children from all the States journeyed to visit this monument to American liberty. Eighty-eight thousand had visited her in 1890. In 1928, 450,000 came. Today, twice that many visit her each year.

In 1931 a new and more modern floodlighting system was installed and Liberty and her pedestal received a long-needed bath to remove the smoke and grime that encrusted her. Her soft green protective coat was not disturbed. At the same time, other needed repairs on the statue were made, including the replacement of the elevator which had been in service in the pedestal for twenty-five years.

Two years later, by order of President Franklin Delano Roosevelt, the administration of the Statue of Liberty was transferred from the War Department to the National Park Service of the Department of Interior. The transfer included only the two-and-a-half acres of Bedloe's Island on which the Star Fort and the statue stood. The major portion of the island was retained for use by the War Department.

Auguste's desire had always been that the entire island be set aside for Liberty. In 1890 he wrote to Butler: "My idea has always been that the island would be, in the future, a kind of Pantheon for the glories of American independence. That you would build around the monument of Liberty the statues of your great men and collect there all the noble memories. This island should become a sort of pilgrimage, a charming walk. . . "

The National Park Service felt, too, that the entire island was none too large to provide a proper setting for the Statue of Liberty. They immediately set about making plans for the future to enlarge the National Monument to include the whole island. These plans, of course, could not be carried out so long as there was dual jurisdiction of Bedloe's.

Meantime, the fiftieth anniversary of Liberty's dedication was approaching. The National Park Service decided to honor Liberty with a nationwide celebration throughout the year 1936. The objective of the program, as officially stated was: "To recall to the minds of the American people the history and significance of the Statue of Liberty and to give as many of them as possible an opportunity to take part in some activity connected with the anniversary observance."

Throughout the year, the history and meaning of the Statue of Liberty were studied by America's school children. Various organizations sponsored essay and poetry contests. Newspapers, magazines, and radio programs gave nationwide publicity to Liberty's golden anniversary.

On October 28, 1936, 3,500 people, including the President of the United States, Franklin Delano Roosevelt, journeyed to Bedloe's Island to attend Miss Liberty's birthday party. From France came the French Under Secretary of State, François de Tessan, and the Mayor of Colmar, Edouard Richard and his young daughter, Marguerite. Thousands throughout the entire United States heard the proceedings on their radios.

As in 1886, Bedloe's was bedecked in red, white, and blue bunting. Everywhere American and French flags waved. There was a tremendous water parade of gayly decorated government, commercial, and private boats.

Whistles shrieked, guns boomed, and bands played. Added to the 1936 celebration were squadrons of army and navy planes that roared overhead.

When President Roosevelt arrived to take his place on the speaker's stand which faced the statue, an American flag was slowly hoisted to Liberty's uplifted hand. Beside the President was the French Ambassador to America, André de Laboulaye, grandson of Edouard de Laboulaye, father of the idea of the "monument of two nations."

As part of the ceremony, a speech by French President Albert Lebrun was broadcast from France. "For fifty years the torch upheld by the Goddess of Liberty has glowed upon the greatest undertakings of man," said Lebrun. "For Liberty is not merely the source of all moral values but also the spring of all creative genius. Now, as then, we believe that liberty is the indispensable requisite of progress, as well as the best safeguard of the future of our democracies."

When the ceremony was over, the Mayor of Colmar and his daughter placed at the base of the statue a wreath of pine and holly that they had brought all the way from Bartholdi's garden in Colmar.

Public interest in the statue continued to grow. The National Park Service was more anxious than ever to transform Bedloe's Island into a place of beauty. A year after Liberty's golden jubilee, the President issued a proclamation adding all the island to the National Monument. Shortly after, needed repairs and painting inside the statue were undertaken by the National Park Service. Liberty's arm, which had been closed to the public since the Black Tom explosion, was strengthened and the spikes in her crown were removed in order to replace their rusted supports. A master plan for beautifying the island was prepared by the National Park Service.

Development of the plan, however, was halted on December 7, 1941 when America entered World War II. The statue itself was blacked out for the duration of the war, except for a tiny aerial obstruction light in her torch. Before the war came to an end, improvements were again made in the lighting system and on May 7, 1945, V-E Day, Miss Liberty shone in greater glory than ever before.

The *Miss Liberty* ferry boat arriving at the Statue

Since the end of the War, the master plan of the National Park Service, designed to put the statue in a setting of well-ordered dignity, has gradually been carried forward.

The cherished dreams Auguste Bartholdi held for his big daughter Liberty are coming true. The name of her little island, which Bartholdi always referred to as "Liberty Island," was officially changed in 1956 from "Bedloe's" to "Liberty." Now the grounds around her are attractively landscaped. The dilapidated old shacks that once surrounded her have been replaced by simple, dignified administration, souvenir, and refreshment buildings.

Auguste Bartholdi said: "Liberty Island is obviously destined to be made into a pleasure ground for the soul of the American people, a place of pilgrimage for citizens of the whole nation." He made that statement in the year 1890. Today, winter and summer, spring and fall, every day of every year, eager American men, women, and children board the Miss Liberty ferry boat to pay a visit to the greatest symbol of freedom the world has ever known, "Liberty Enlightening the World."

THE STATUE OF LIBERTY

Dimensions

	FEET	INCHES
Height from foundation of pedestal to torch	305	1
Height from base to torch	151	1
Height of granite pedestal	89	0
Height of foundation	65	0
Length of hand	16	5
Length of index finger	8	0
Size of fingernail, 13 x 10 inches		
Thickness of head from ear to ear	10	0
Distance across the eye	2	0
Length of nose	4	6
Width of mouth	3	0
Length of right arm	42	0
Thickness of waist	35	0

Weight

	POUNDS	
Copper	200,000	(100 tons)
Steel	250,000	(125 tons)
Total weight	450,000	(225 tons)

ACKNOWLEDGMENTS

I AM grateful to all those who were so very helpful to me in the preparation of this book.

Officials of the National Parks Service were most cooperative in allowing me access to unpublished material and collections of pictures. In the Washington, D.C. office, I am deeply indebted to Rogers W. Young, Branch of History, for his advice and help on source material and to Ralph H. Anderson, Branch of Information, for his assistance in assembling pictures. Col. Randle B. Truett, Chief Park Historian, Lincoln Museum, was especially helpful on my research concerning the medal for Mrs. Lincoln. At the Statue of Liberty National Monument, I received assistance from Newell Foster, Superintendent, Dr. Thomas M. Pitkin, Chief Park Historian, Louis Morris, Historian, and Simeon Horace Pickering, Tour Leader Supervisor. I wish to thank Dr. Walter E. Hugins, Jr., Park Historian, Morristown National Military Park, for the use of unpublished material on the improvements at the Statue of Liberty.

Staff members of libraries and other associations greatly facilitated my research. Valuable assistance was given me throughout the Library of Congress. I am especially grateful to Miss Virginia Daiker, Prints and Photographs, for her valuable aid in helping me to assemble pictures. I am indebted to the Manuscripts Division for the use of original letters and also to the Music Department for information concerning Gounod's music. For other valuable material I am indebted to The New York Public Library, New York City, to the Art Department of The Free Library of Philadelphia, to George Pettengill, Librarian, American Institute of Architects, and to Mrs. Geraldine P. Staub, Curator, Drexel Institute of Technology. I wish also to thank Dr. André Gschaedler, Historian, Chairman of the Bartholdi Committee of L'union Alsacienne of New York, for his many helpful suggestions.

I am most grateful for the assistance given me by Jacques Betz, Bibliothécaire à la Bibliothèque Nationale, Paris, and by Vladimir Fédorov, Le Bibliothécaire, Bibliothèque du Conservatoire de Musique, Bibliothèque Nationale. I wish to express appreciation to Pierre Schmitt, Le Conservateur, Bibliothèque, Colmar, France. My research in Paris was greatly facilitated by my good friends Madame Simone Le Marchand and Mrs. Lewis R. Collins.

To René L. Wenger, Head of the French Department, St. Stephen's School for Boys, Alexandria, Virginia and to my dear friend Mrs. Douglas H. Dies, I owe a real debt of gratitude for many hours of help in translating reference material.

The entire work was made possible through the patient guidance and encouragement which I received from Mrs. Lillian McClintock, Editor, Children's Books, Rand McNally and Company.

Willadene Price

INDEX

A

Agnes (statue of), 17

Album du Bord (book of cartoons by Bartholdi), 95

Alsace, Province of, 55, 57, 88, 117, 168

American Pedestal Fund Committee: founded, 104; notifies Bartholdi of action of Congress, 105; plans to circulate subscription, 106; fund raising by, 119; Art Loan Exhibition of, 121–122; unable to proceed with pedestal, 137; announces resumption of work, 140; plans dedication ceremonies, 145; difficulties with lighting of statue, 154–155; honored at banquet, 154; members serve with Citizens' Committee, 164

Amérique, SS, 95, 140

Army, Department of, 164

Art Loan Exhibition, 121–122

Astor, William Waldorf, 148

B

Balloon (statue), 167

Bartholdi, Amédée (cousin), 95–96

Bartholdi, Charles (brother), 11–13, 16, 17, 25

Bartholdi, Charlotte Beysser (mother): description of, 13, 41, 47, 58; takes sons to Paris for schooling, 15–16; allows Auguste to pursue career in art, 19–20; affection of, for Auguste, 25; at inauguration of Rapp statue, 30; at inauguration of Bruat statue, 33; reaction of, to war, 47, 50–51, 55, 58; birthday celebration of, 51; and Auguste's trip to America, 57, 59; as model for Statue of Liberty's face, 78, 86; worries about Bartholdi, 88; meets daughter-in-law, 105; celebrates 81st birthday, 114; visits Statue of Liberty, 115; greets Victor Hugo, 128, suffers illness, 146; 158–159; celebrates 90th birthday, 159; death of, 160

Printed in U.S.A.